Joy of Heeling

Building Confidence, Enthusiasm and Precision through Games

by Julie Flanery

Published by Creative Canine LLC

Copyright ©2022 Julie Flanery

Design, Layout and Graphics by:

Teresa Hall

Editing by:

Gail Beerman

Limits of Liability and Disclaimer of Warranty:
The author and publisher shall not be liable in the event of incidental or consequential damages in connection with or arising out of, the furnishing, performance, or use of the instructions and suggestions contained in this book.

Printed in the United States of America

ISBN: 979-8-9868770-0-6

PRAISE FOR "JOY OF HEELING"

As a hardcore enthusiast of "all things heeling", I can recommend Julie, her methods and her games without reservation. Julie is a master at taking a complex skill fraught with challenge and turning it into a joyful expression of teamwork. If you want more joyful and precise heeling for rally, obedience or freestyle, this book will guide you from your very first training session to …"Wow! That's my dog!

-Denise Fenzi, Founder, Fenzi Dog Sports Academy

I've had the pleasure of working with Julie and teaching the games and exercises in Joy of Heeling with two very different dogs of my own. A Golden Retriever and a Schipperke. It was revelatory in different ways for each of them.

Joy of Heeling is a win-win for both dog and handler, creating joy for the work in the dog and joy for the handler in teaching the work. With a wide variety of games and skills to use at different points in the training process, you can be certain that neither the dog, nor the handler, will get bored, or tired of doing the same old thing.

Having this book available to review basic steps, and reminders of how to advance behaviors will be a wonderful addition to my training library.

Joy of Heeling is clearly written, entertaining, and easy to follow, I highly recommend it to new trainers, and those who have been training for a long time. It will become one of your favorite training books, filled with insights on training in general and not just heeling!

-Esther Zimmerman, competition obedience instructor

What a refreshing approach for teaching heelwork! As a freestyler, Julie brings many new and fun approaches to traditional obedience training. All the games I've learned and loved from Julie can be found between these covers! Lift, movement, energy are all common themes throughout the book. Julie has created a framework for training so that as she says: "Heeling predicts games and games predict heeling".

Her focus on the many facets of reinforcement and reward events is appreciated. Without the right type, frequency and value, it would be difficult to develop Julie's coined phrase of creating a "Happy Emotional Response" (HER) to heelwork. Not only will you come away with great heeling games, but her concepts and general training advice will also apply to ALL training!!

This book is written with the same joy and expertise that you find when working with Julie in person. She embodies joy in all that she does, especially her joy of heeling! I am so glad to have this book in my collection.

-Julie Symons, owner of Savvy Dog Sports

PREFACE

I am a trainer. Let me start by saying that this book is not the "be-all and end-all" of teaching a dog to heel. There are many highly skilled trainers out there who have a far better grasp of the technical components of heelwork than I do! So if you are looking for a book that focuses primarily on the precision aspects of heeling, this isn't it! While there are many games and exercises included here that will teach your dog to heel with precision and accuracy, that is not my primary focus.

The focus of this book is to highlight the impact and importance of how our dog's emotional or mental association with the practice and act of heeling affects the outcome of our training, and how both dog and handler feel about heeling.

We know that training should be enjoyable for both the dog and the handler. This expectation may be why so many avoid heeling altogether, dread it even! While many skills that we teach can be innately enjoyable to the dog, heeling is rarely one of them. My hope is that this book shows you a path where heeling becomes one of your dog's favorite activities, and yours, as well!

I am a freestyler. While I didn't start out my dog sport career in musical freestyle, it has shaped my training processes unlike any other sport I've competed in. And there have been several. Being competitive by nature, I've been lucky enough to have had the opportunity to title in several dog sports including obedience, agility and Rally, as well as musical freestyle, heelwork-to-music and Rally-FrEe.

What these experiences have taught me is that without our dog opting in, finding joy in the training and the performance, I will never find satisfaction or joy in competing in dog sports. Period.

When I first started out in musical freestyle, I was glad to leave the world of obedience and the necessary heeling behind. Heeling was my nemesis. I didn't enjoy doing it or training it. One reason I went into freestyle was so I wouldn't have to heel anymore! Tricks are fun! Exciting! And Joyful! Little did I know, and would later learn that freestyle also included the necessity of heeling. And heeling too can be fun! Exciting! And joyful!

As I again started to work on my dog's heeling, I realized that what I had been feeling was less about the actual behavior and more about how it was approached. At that time, the dog's enjoyment of a learned skill was not part of the equation. Walking in a large circle in "dog obedience" class, my dog at my side, hoping beyond hope that at some point she would miraculously offer something I could reward was not my, nor my dog's idea of a good time.

I am a learner. Positive reinforcement based training opened new avenues for many trainers, including me. We still have so much to learn though in how to use reinforcement in a way that not only increases the likelihood of behavior but raises the emotional response to a point where it is physically manifested in the appearance of joy. Especially when it comes to heelwork.

By changing the way I train heelwork, and putting my dog's enjoyment of the process first, I have come to not only love heelwork but embrace it as a way to tap into my dog's emotional and physical energy and showcase our personal and training relationship. It is that change in priority that makes us both feel engaged, connected and joyful!

My goal is that you, too, can prioritize the enjoyment you and your dog feel when heeling, and to view the games and exercises that bring about that enjoyment as not just foundational, but essential in your heelwork training.

I am a teacher. So many seem to want that joyful picture of heeling yet still seem to cling to methods that focus primarily on precision and accuracy, without exploring the relevance of the dog's emotional response and how that impacts the final result. I want to share what I have learned and developed with others! That's what teachers do! We share so that others may benefit. My hope is that you, too will share what you learn here, so that more teams may find the Joy of Heeling.

TABLE OF CONTENTS

Part I JOY

Part II Let The Games Begin

Part IV More Games! More Joy!

Part V Developing Grit: Games, Resilience, Integration, Teamwork

PART I

Joy

/JOI/ NOUN
1. A FEELING OF GREAT PLEASURE AND HAPPINESS

CHAPTER 1:

INTRODUCTION TO JOY OF HEELING

"Joy of Heeling" – For many, this phrase may seem to be an oxymoron. While joy is the physical and emotional expression of enjoyment and happiness, heeling is physically and mentally demanding, requiring considerable concentration, precision, and accuracy. How can these qualities merge to create what so many of us aspire to?

Yet we know it is attainable. We see it in those electrifying dog-and-handler teams that inspire us, motivate us and give us the picture, the vision of what heeling could be.

The challenge then is to balance and blend these seemingly contradictory attributes into a singular skill that we call heeling. To craft our training sessions in a way that our dog chooses the games and exercises that create that perfect picture of joyful and precise heeling.

Choosing Heelwork

As with any activity, there is an emotional component that dictates whether we or our dogs choose to engage in that activity, now or in the future. For many handlers, heelwork is way down on their list of enjoyable skills to train; I am sure many dogs also feel the same way. That can change though, through our approach to training and the type and manner of reinforcement we provide.

This book is a compilation of the games and exercises I use to create my vision of joyful heeling. A vision that includes the outward appearance of confidence, enthusiasm, willingness and yes, joy.

Some I have learned from others, and some I have developed from the training of other behaviors. And of course, the most joyful have been the ones that my dogs have claimed as their own – those games and exercises that were developed out of their love and enjoyment of certain activities – those activities that when given a choice, are what they choose.

All of the exercises outlined in this book, whether the construct or foundation games or the accuracy and precision exercises are meant to be ongoing. You won't stop playing the construct games when you start your precision exercises. They all work together and complement each other nicely.

The more games and exercises you play, the more information and reinforcement history the dog gains for both criteria of "joy" and "precision." Your dog will start to bring these two criteria together and will start to offer that picture of beautiful heelwork. Watch for it! Reinforce it! That is the moment you will start to realize what the Joy of Heeling is all about.

> ### What is Lift?
>
> *You will hear me refer to "lift" quite a bit. In reference to heelwork, lift is a lightness on the dog's forelegs and front feet derived from the dog shifting their weight to the rear, resulting in the lifting of their head and chest. It is often accompanied by a slight bounce or prance.*

High Expectations vs True Potential

Your dog's capability and capacity for high energy heeling, with lift and animation, may or may not be in line with your expectations. If your dog isn't one that shows a level of animation, energy, enthusiasm, dynamism, and excitement in everyday life and interactions, i.e. outside of training and heelwork, then it's not something we can artificially produce.

The energy comes from the dog – the motivation comes from the games and reinforcement the handler provides. If your dog is normally lower energy or has a high threshold for excitement–meaning it takes a lot in the real world to get them excited, then the expectation that they will get really excited about heeling may be unrealistic. That starts with motivation and reinforcement at a more basic level.

What's important is that we look at our dog's true potential – that we draw out the best our dog has to offer. That we use reinforcement and movement and games to build motivation and joy. And that will look a little different for every dog. If you are expecting your dog to move like a Malinois or a Border Collie or a Golden and you have a Scottish Terrier or a Basset Hound or a Keeshond, (or a funky structured mixed breed like one of mine!) your expectation may hinder your dog's true potential.

Every dog is different. What is the same, no matter the dog, is that we provide them a reason, a strong motivation, to play this silly game we call heeling. So that when given the choice, you both experience a feeling of excitement and anticipation at the chance to heel.

Two Pieces of the Puzzle

There are two general components of heelwork: **Precision and Dynamism**. These two pieces fit together to help make the complete picture.

Precision is the accuracy and correctness of your position criteria. Where do you want the dog to be in relation to your body? This is not the same for all dogs and handlers, nor is it the same for all organizations or sports. The American Kennel Club, Canadian Kennel Club and other kennel clubs around the world that offer competition obedience have a specific place they want your dog to be. And moreover, where they don't want your dog to be.

In other dog sports, such as freestyle or Rally-FrEe, the handler chooses their heel position. The criteria are that the dog's position in relation to the handler stays consistent and that some part of the dog and handler's bodies must overlap. That's not to say that the position is imprecise or inaccurate. Only that it is customized to each dog and handler team. I like my dogs to forge a little, that is, their head is slightly ahead of me with my leg about at their shoulder. Freestylers with smaller dogs may want their dogs to work a little wide. So if you are working in freestyle, keep that in mind.

Freestylers work their dogs on both the right and the left sides with the same heeling criteria. While you are not required to do so in other ring sports such as obedience, I do believe it is beneficial to the dog to be even or symmetrical in their muscle development and use, so even though you might be working left-side heeling for your sport of choice, you might decide to add some right-side work to your repertoire.

Either way, it will be important that you know what the position requirements are for whichever sport or organization you will be competing under before you start training. You will want to determine and then visualize the position criteria you want to communicate to your dog. Where is their head? where is their rear? How far are they from you? Are they straight? These are your technical criteria.

Dynamism is the energy, vitality, and enthusiasm that your dog puts into the act of heeling. It is indicated through an energy, keenness, willingness, and readiness. This can manifest in a lift of the chest and lightness on the feet. The head is up and ears set forward. There is a "brightness" to the eyes. Some components of dynamism may feel indescribable – they are the emotional components we want our dogs to feel while heeling. This is joy.

I teach precision and dynamism separately at the start. As they are reinforced separately, you will see each criterion and each component merge together during the exercises. In essence, your dog will bring the dynamism and the precision together, borne from a high rate of reinforcement and value for each, creating

a more full and complete picture of joyful heeling.

That doesn't mean that you shouldn't see happy emotions when training the more technical aspects! It just means that in the exercises meant to create dynamism we are not going to require our precision criteria.

Heeling is physically demanding. Structure matters. Your dog's physicality and condition matter.

"By breaking out the pieces that make up beautiful and joyful heelwork we allow the dog, through a history of reinforcement and enjoyment, to bring these pieces together. The result is a naturalness and fluidity of movement and the outward expression of joy that comes from confidence and the expectation of a positive outcome. This is what Joy of Heeling is all about."

It's possible your dog's structure is not suited to the picture of pretty heelwork that you have in your head! That doesn't mean your dog can't put out some rockin' heelwork! Only that you may have to adjust your picture to the most their structure is able to offer.

Your dog may have great structure but may still need some conditioning, stretching, or muscle strength to give you what you want.

Heeling is mentally demanding. Reinforcement matters. Your ability to motivate your dog matters.

Be generous. Your rate of reinforcement and the value your dog finds in the rewards you provide have a direct impact on your dog's desire to work at heeling. More is better. If you feel like you are rewarding too much you are doing just fine!

In the next couple of chapters, we'll be exploring exercises to assess and increase your dog's physical ability and reinforcement value to maximize your results.

CHAPTER 2:
Reinforcement and Reward Events

Reinforcement: What It is and What It is Not

In training, we have options as to what methods to use. There are many ways to "get the behavior" and there are many ways to teach heelwork.

Luring, shaping, targeting, and capturing are some of the methods that dog sport trainers are either familiar with or have experience with. Methods lead the way. They provide a means for us to communicate to our dogs how to earn reinforcement. It's important to remember though that the method is only as effective as the reinforcement. It is reinforcement that affects the outcome.

You've likely heard the phrase "Reinforcement drives behavior." What exactly does that mean? While there are specific scientific definitions of the word "reinforcement," if we pull out our trusty Webster's dictionary it gives us the layman's usage, which in this case is pretty similar to the way trainers and behaviorists use the term.

Webster defines reinforcement as:

1: the action of strengthening or encouraging something: the state of being reinforced

2: something that strengthens or encourages something, a response to someone's behavior that is intended to make that person more likely to behave that way again.

3: psychology: the action of causing a subject to learn to give or to increase the frequency of the desired response that involves the use of a reward following a correct response

For our use, let's define reinforcement as:

Anything that increases the likelihood, frequency, or quality of behavior in a learner.

What about rewards? Let's head back to our trusty Webster's dictionary:

1: something that is given in return for good or evil done or received or that is offered or given for some service or attainment

2: a stimulus (such as food) that is administered to an organism and serves to reinforce a desired response

There is a subtle but distinct difference between "rewards" and "reinforcement." In essence, we might give the dog something as a reward – something that we think "serves to reinforce" – say, a piece of food, but unless we observe an increase in the quality or frequency of the behavior, it's not actually reinforcement. Eating food is not indicative that behavior is being reinforced. If no part of the behavior improved, it's just free food.

Be mindful of what you are using as rewards. Be observant as to whether the quality or frequency of the behavior is increasing. This will impact your training outcomes, both in the time it takes to train the behavior, and the quality of the work.

Our goal in providing reinforcement is not just to increase the quality or frequency of our heelwork criteria – the precision, accuracy, proximity. We also want to create a conditioned emotional response (CER) to our heelwork training – not just any CER though! We want an HER! A Happy Emotional Response! And so, we want to be particularly thoughtful about our rewards.

As with all reinforcement, the learner, in this case, our dog, sets the value. It's our job to observe and use what causes an increase in the quality or frequency of our heeling criteria, and what brings our dogs joy. We can then apply that knowledge to our training.

I will be referring to rewards and reinforcement or reinforcer interchangeably, assuming that you are being observant and that the rewards you provide are actually having the desired effect in increasing the quality or frequency of the behavior or criterion and creating an HER.

Definitions and Types of Reinforcement

Without diving too deeply into scientific definitions of reinforcement, I'll be using some terms we'll want to agree upon. These definitions align with those commonly used in dog training and are not meant to be conclusive.

"Eating food is not indicative of reinforcement. If no part of the behavior is improved or increased, it's just free food."

We've defined reinforcement as anything that causes an increase in the quality or frequency of a behavior. Within this definition, we can further categorize reinforcement as "**primary**" or "**secondary**."

Primary reinforcement is that reinforcement which occurs naturally and does not need to be learned to be of value. In general, they are considered needed for survival. A common list of primary reinforcement is water, food, sleep, and sex.

In the dog training world, "primary reinforcement" has been expanded to include activities such as certain types of play, including chase or tug (which could be construed as part of the food-seeking process). The most commonly used reinforcers in dog training are food or play, though these are certainly not the only reinforcers that can be used to increase desirable behavior.

Secondary reinforcers, also referred to as conditioned reinforcers, are those reinforcers where the value has been learned. While certain types of play could be considered primary reinforcement, the toy itself is a secondary or conditioned reinforcer.

Secondary reinforcers predict primary reinforcement and can create an emotional response related to the anticipation of that primary reinforcement. In the same way that a clicker (secondary reinforcer) predicts a food reward (primary reinforcer) and our dogs become excited at the sight or sound of the clicker – they have also learned that the appearance of a toy predicts the resulting play activity and they become excited and even joyful at the prospect of play.

Why am I telling you this? You are reading this because you want a dog that finds joy in the especially difficult task of heeling. The way to create that joy and attach it to the skill of heeling is in what and how we reinforce. To apply the processes that are outlined in this book, you will benefit from understanding the dynamics of primary and secondary reinforcement.

What's Love Got to Do With It? Everything!

You'll be using a variety of rewards and reinforcement, both primary and secondary, to build the skill and the enjoyment of heelwork. In some, you will build value by pairing it with a primary reinforcer such as food. Others will be natural activities in which your dog finds joy, such as running, chasing, jumping, or playing.

Tangible rewards, such as food or toys, and non-tangible rewards such as play and engagement in certain activities, produce an enjoyable emotional state. If we pair a behavior such as heeling with those things that bring our dogs joy or pleasure, that emotion will bleed into their heelwork. If heelwork predicts those things our dogs love, enjoy, find value in, then heelwork becomes not only a secondary reinforcer but its association with that emotional state increases our dog's love of heeling.

Do you have a list of those things – types of food, toys, interactions, or activities that you observe your dog truly "loves" and seeks out? In choosing reinforcement, the value of what you choose to use as reward should not only be in direct correlation to the difficulty of the task, and the emotions we want to evoke, but also in the value you place on the behavior. If the behavior is important to you, reinforce it in a way that makes that evident.

While I will provide you with exercises that spark joy and energy for most dogs, you will learn to create games that are unique to you and your dog. That may sound difficult now, but as you work through the exercises, as you become more in tune with what your dog finds joy in, you will be able to use your own unique games to build value and joy in your heelwork training.

While some rewards can be too low in value to keep the dog motivated, there can also be too much value in the rewards you are providing. Your dog can become overly aroused, hard-mouthed, thinking too much about the physical act of getting the reward rather than being thoughtful about why it will be provided.

"Every time you teach your dog what to do, you teach them how to feel."
~ Amy Cook, PhD

Just as you have that picture in your head of beautiful heeling, you'll want that picture of beautiful focus, where your dog is attentive, engaged, willing, and ready (can you picture it?), but not over the top. We can manipulate that state through our choices of rewards and making sure we are at that "goldilocks" value. But! If you must err one way or the other, err on the side of too much value. It's easier to adjust downward than upward, both in the value of reward and in the demeanor or arousal of the dog.

What we provide as rewards not only needs to create a happy emotional state but also needs to act as reinforcement for the more technical aspects of heelwork. To ensure that what you are providing is reinforcing your technical criteria, you'll want to keep a record of your progress, even if that record is just the videos you've taken (name and date each one so that you can review your progress). If you aren't seeing improvement in a particular aspect of your heelwork, then you'll want to assess your criteria, reinforcement, or timing of your marker. Adjusting one or all of these can quickly provide information about what your dog needs to be more successful in meeting your criteria.

What the Heck is a Marker, and do I Need to Use One?

A marker is a bridge that spans the gap between the behavior or criterion and the reinforcer. In its simplest form, it communicates to the dog why they are being rewarded.

Many trainers describe what happens at the time of the marker as a "snapshot in time;" the point in which behavior occurs or a criterion is met, that earns the reward.

Following a behavior or criterion, a lot can happen in the time it takes the reward to be delivered. It's possible and sometimes even likely that our dogs can associate the reward with something that we had no intention of reinforcing and we were unaware of the effect our reward was having.

A marker, when provided at the time the behavior occurs or the criterion is met, indicates why reinforcement is being provided. This "moment of why" provides the dog with the information they need to repeat the behavior or criteria. The timing of your marker is key in helping the dog understand not only why the reward was provided but how to make it happen again.

What makes a marker valuable? A marker is always followed by and therefore predicts the primary reward. This pairing makes the marker a secondary reinforcer. The knowledge and anticipation of receiving primary reward creates that happy emotional state we want to develop in our heeling.

A marker also allows for the time it takes for the handler to retrieve the reward from wherever it's being stored – pocket, bait bag, nearby table, etc. – that time ensures that the reward is not present until after the marker, to maintain its predictive value.

Many of the games and exercises will include the use of markers to predict primary reinforcement and to build value in what occurred at the time of the marker.

Types of Markers

One of the more commonly used markers is a clicker, a small, hand-held device that emits a sharp, distinct sound.

There are other means of marking behavior, including verbal markers, such as "yes" or "good." There are location or reward-specific markers which provide additional information to the dog such as the location or type of reinforcement and there are physical markers such as reaching for a reward or beginning your reward event by praising or pulling out a toy. A specific facial expression can also act as a marker if it is consistently followed by reinforcement.

They all do the same thing. Markers link an action or criterion to reinforcement. Your marker not only predicts a reward but also tells the dog why the reward is coming, giving them a reason to repeat what occurred at the moment in time the marker occurred.

"The more clear I become in my mechanics the faster her tail wags!"
~ Teresa and Holly

Your marker is most effective when it is distinct, novel and separated from other stimuli. Overlapping the delivery of reward with the marker will diminish it's effectiveness, making the value of the marker moot. There is no predictive value then if the marker and reinforcement are delivered simultaneously.

Intentional vs Unintentional Markers

Reaching for your reward or starting to deliver a reward is often an unintentional marker. While it is effective in marking behavior, we don't necessarily want our dogs focused on whether we are going to be reaching for our pocket or bait bag. This is why I refer to it as an unintentional marker.

As you work through the games and exercises, we will be using a "touch and treat" hand target as opposed to a sustained hand target. It will be part of building your criteria, act as a reinforcer, and can act as a marker for your dog's correct responses. While it still involves moving your hand, it is much more intentional than reaching for your pocket or bait bag.

Reinforcement Strategies

Reinforcement strategies can help to define the behavior for the dog. They may involve specific placement, either to set the dog up for the next repetition (reset) or to encourage specific criteria for future reps. Or they may be delivered in such a way as to create an emotional response that can be attached to the behavior.

A reward not only serves to reinforce the behavior and create an emotional state, but how and where it is delivered can impact your goal behavior almost as much as your marker.

A reward that is placed higher, such as from the handler's hand over the dog's head, causes the dog's energy to move upward. The chest lifts, the front feet may come off the ground. A pattern of feeding high can create this physical reaction in anticipation of the reward.

Reward placement doesn't change what has already occurred. If after I mark, I place a treat to the outside of the dog's head while in heel position, it isn't meant to lure the dog's head out so that their rear tucks in tighter *then*, but rather to encourage proper positioning in *future* repetitions.

If the dog realizes a pattern, that the food is always placed to the outside of their head for coming into heel position, they will start to adjust their

Fast Food and Fine Dining

Your reinforcement can have greater impact than just increasing the quality or frequency of a behavior. How, where and when it's delivered can influence future behavior.

Fast Food and Fine Dining are two techniques I use to build value, increase duration, and have an emotional impact on the dog.

Fast Food is just what it sounds like. It is one treat after another, after another in rapid succession. I use it to build value in positions such as heel, front, or down, or locations, such as a bed or crate. The duration is short – the time it takes to feed five or six treats one at a time - and is followed by either a release cue or is used in conjunction with Fine Dining to add duration.

In Fine Dining, I still feed several treats in a row, but it is at a much slower rate. There is time and space between the reinforcement that helps to build duration and the dog's understanding that reward is not always immediate. It, too, is always followed by a release cue.

body in future repetitions so that getting to the reward is more efficient. Alternately, feeding with the far hand, across my body, can encourage my dog's head to turn toward me and can pull their rear away from me. The dog's goal is to get to reward. They will figure out how to adjust their body and the entry into the position, in a way that allows them to do that efficiently.

If I have my dog jump up to get a treat during heeling and they expect that they will need to jump a little to get the reward, then they will start to anticipate that and prepare their body to collect the reward. The dog's head will look upward, their chest will lift and their rear will lower to be ready to push off.

This is the value of strategic reward placement. The dog learns to move their body in a way that benefits behavior in subsequent reps because it benefits their access to reinforcement.

As I am helping to create these physical changes through my pattern of reward delivery, it gives me something to mark and reward in future reps. If every 3 steps, I let my dog jump up a little for a treat or hand touch, they will start to prepare their body just before the 3rd step. When I see that, I can mark and then present the food for them to jump to, re-starting the pattern. I can then start to extend the number of steps.

It sounds pretty slick and clean! It will actually look a little messy! That's okay! All I care about is that my dog is expecting to jump a little to get food (or touch my hand) and that I am ready to mark that. I don't care about the precision or accuracy of position at this point.

Reward Events – Value Added

Reward events are how we can make an exercise, a behavior, or a sequence more valuable and increase the dog's desire to continue to engage in the training, even ask for more. It is part of how we add a joyful emotional state to our heelwork - or any training. Spend time and effort making your rewards and reward events fun for your dog. The games you'll be learning not only increase your dog's heeling skills but become part of your reward events.

Often, we tend to reward by rote. We reward the same way, often with the same thing and for the same amount of time. We assume that because our dog eats the treat, or takes the tug, it is reinforcing. Remember that reinforcement causes an increase in the quality or frequency of a behavior. As trainers, we want to constantly assess improvement or lack of improvement. If we are seeing a lack of improvement, we need to determine if it is due to our ineffective communication (is your criteria appropriate and your marker well-timed?) or due to the lack of value of the reinforcement we are providing.

Heeling is hard work. If we want our dogs to be enthusiastic heelers then our reinforcement needs to be more than a cursory piece of food. The pay needs to be commensurate with the level of work. The more we ask of our dog, the more reward we need to be willing to provide.

Rather than giving your dog one treat, give them several in a row, *Fast Food* style, one right after the other, paired with verbal praise.

Most dogs would rather move than remain stationary. Allowing them to use their bodies in receiving rewards can increase the value of the reward. I will often have my dog jump a little to get the treat, either in front of me as I move backward or next to me as I move forward.

There are many ways that you can add value to your reinforcement through the way it is delivered.

Tossing food for your dog to chase is a great way to add movement to both your dog and the reward. For a dog, it's much more fun to chase and eat food than to just eat food!

Run with your dog to reinforcement, whether it's in a dish on a table or whether you just tossed it. A game of Race Me, Chase Me can add excitement and value to the reward.

Flirt poles, tug games, favorite tricks, and fetch can all be used as part of reinforcement. Food rewards, toy play, and personal play can all be combined as part of a reward event.

Dogs have preferences. Be sure you know what they are. Note that the value of reinforcement is not static. Value can change in the short or long term, depending on the environment, the dog's satiation, the difficulty of the task, how it's delivered, and how long you've been using it.

It's why we include fun and games. They are part of the reinforcement. The games you will learn here can and should be included in your reward events.

Value Diminished

Value can be added, and value can also be diminished. When the value of reinforcement is diminished, we may still see an increase in behavior, though we aren't as likely to see that HER, the joy that we are trying to create in our heeling.

Value can be diminished in a variety of ways. And this list is not all-inclusive, rather just a few examples so that you can be better aware of how value can be affected.

If the value of the reinforcement is less than expected, say your dog was expecting food and you brought out a toy, then we may see a decrease in our dog's HER. Or maybe you have a mix of rewards in your pocket and the last few were cheese, and then you give a piece of kibble – you can see how that might create some disappointment for some dogs. If you have been using salty or dry rewards such as hot dogs or dehydrated treats, it's likely that at some point in the session these will no longer maintain their value and water will have more value than these types of "rewards." We could even go so far as to say that they may even become aversive to the dog.

The environment and how we use our body or our voice can affect value. Praise and even tactile interaction with our dogs is often welcomed, though for some dogs that can lower the value of the reward. Sudden, loud praise, "big arms", reaching toward or leaning over our dogs can elicit a negative response, or change our dog's emotional state, rendering our well-intentioned reward less than rewarding.

Optimum Economics

When working the stationary or precision exercises it's important that the value of the reinforcement is equal to or greater than the difficulty of the task. The longer or harder the exercise, the longer the duration or the sequence, the more reward value we need to provide - not just in the value or quantity of food (though that can be part of it), but also the duration of the reward, the emotion, and genuineness we put into it - the entire reward event. Think of it as behavior economics. Heeling is an expensive behavior, not just in quality and quantity of reward but also in the cost of maintenance over the career of your dog.

There is an optimum point in a training session where beyond that, behavior will start to subtly deteriorate. It can be hard, but we really need to be aware of that point. Once we pass that point, the work previous to that is diminished. The "reward" we are providing is no longer reinforcing our criteria and the benefits gained early in the session can be compromised.

 "The more we ask of our dog, the more reward we need to be willing to provide."

In many of the precision exercises we do, we are working with repetition; when your dog is doing well and they are "getting it," it can be hard to break off or end the session. We need to guard against "just one more" so as not to compromise the entire session. Frequent games that allow the dog freedom of movement to offset the work we are asking them to do with their bodies is crucial to maintaining both the physical and the emotional state that we want our dogs in during our training of this most difficult of behaviors.

Challenge Yourself to come up with a variety of rewards that can be included in a longer-lasting "reward event." You don't have to make this complicated — If your dog loves food and tug, use food and tug. If your dog loves to chase then use a flirt pole or toss food 3 or 4 times instead of once or play a game of chase with you being the prey.

I'm not suggesting that you let your dog chase squirrels or go sniff for 10 minutes as part of the reward, but getting to smell something really stinky in a container you have tucked away or licking a bunch of peanut butter off a licky mat, or letting them chase the flirt pole for longer than the time it takes to feed a couple of treats, can make the work you are asking them to do not only worthwhile but something they look forward to.

All of the games that are covered in this book are really just reward events! As you go through the exercises, keep note of the ones your dog really seems to enjoy.

Using Reward Events for the Greatest Impact

Often, handlers use these longer duration reward events at the end of a session. While there is nothing wrong with that, if we are only using them at the end of a session then we aren't taking full advantage of the increase in HER they are producing and can carry into heelwork. By integrating our reward events and games into our heeling sessions, our dogs start to learn that heeling is part of the game.

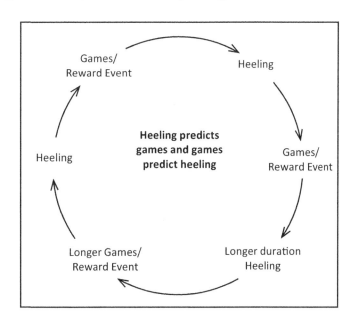

Games/ Reward Event

Heeling

Heeling predicts games and games predict heeling

Heeling

Games/ Reward Event

Longer Games/ Reward Event

Longer duration Heeling

As you work through the games and exercises here, you will gain a better understanding of what that looks like. As mentioned earlier, the harder or longer our dogs work, the greater the value and duration of the reward. By integrating these reward events and games into the session rather than just at the end or only occasionally, heeling becomes part of the game.

For my dogs, that means that after several steps of nice heeling, I mark, then start praising as I reach to get my food reward. Then as I move backward, I offer a treat in front of me at a height they may have to come off the ground slightly or jump a little to get. By having them jump, they are releasing some energy and pressure that may have built from the close precision work. Coming towards me maintains value in me as part of the reward.

It's not over yet! I might then do a little bit of bowling the treat for them to chase. Not once, but several times. For longer duration of heeling, I could reach for my tug or flirt pole for a few rounds. Afterward, I might throw in a butt scrub or ear massage to bring arousal down a little so that I can move back into heeling. And the sequence starts again. **Heeling predicts games and games predict heeling.** Heeling begins to take on the HER associated with the games included in the reward event.

The Value of a Baseline

Seeing gradual change is hard. Recognizing that the work, time, and energy you put in makes a difference, is an important part of all training. Having a baseline that you can look back on can help to reinforce you, for the work you will be doing and will continue to do in your maintenance.

If the shoe fits....

While you may not think of footwear as a game changer when it comes to heeling, wearing the right pair of shoes can make a world of difference for both you and your dog.

As we walk, our feet can compensate for the type of footwear we are wearing. This can affect our gait, making it inconsistent from one session to the next. Wearing sandals can cause us to walk differently than if we are wearing a pair of hiking boots. A pair of flats can cause us to walk differently than wearing a pair of good fitting athletic shoes. Sandals or flats cause us to grip with our toes to keep the heel of the shoe on. Hiking boots tend to flatten our steps, rather than rolling heel to toe.

For heelwork, choose a well-fitting shoe that encompasses your foot securely so there is no worry of it coming off. Make sure there is some flexibility to allow for a heel to toe rocking of the foot. Wearing the right shoe can help add fluidity and consistency to your movement, making it easier for your dog to stay in position.

What have you got? It's okay if the answer is "Nothing!" I bet you have more than you think! Video is invaluable in assessing your skill as well as your dog's. It is objective and doesn't lie!

Consider taking a baseline video before you do any of the exercises.

For your baseline video, you will want enough space to move out about 40-50 ft without needing to turn. Indoors or outdoors is fine.

Your first clip should be what you consider a normal heeling pace for you and your dog. Work in a straight line. Be sure your dog is on the side of the camera. Don't drill this! Just give it one or two passes. Be sure to video!

One of the challenges of heelwork is having enough space to move out at a speed and rhythm that your dog is truly comfortable with. I remember clearly my first obedience instructor telling me "if it feels like you are moving too fast, it's just right for your dog." Granted, this depends a little on the size and normal gait of the dog. It's still a good piece of advice. In most cases, we move too slowly for our dogs. And that can create some discomfort and possibly some annoyance affecting our dog's emotional state and how they feel about heelwork.

After your first baseline video, take another in the same place, on the same day, but with increased speed. Not running or jogging, just a longer and/or faster stride. How does it feel? How does your dog look when you move out a little more?

Too fast for you? Our dogs can be a bit flexible. Each of you may have to compromise a little when it comes to speed to find what works best for both of you. Keep in mind though that you are only half of the team. So, consider your dog's needs as well as your own.

As a freestyler, music is an integral part of what we do. Using music, the tempo or beat, or pulse, will often slow us down or speed us up. You can use music to help you maintain a consistent pace or speed – even if you are the only one hearing it in earbuds. The more consistent your pace while training your heelwork, the happier your dog will be, especially if that speed allows them freedom of movement. Not everyone is comfortable using music or hearing the beat. But if you are, give it a try. It will help you stay consistent and that, in turn, will help your dog.

Using a metronome can also provide a steady beat to synchronize your steps and create consistency in your pace. There are several apps for downloading on your phone that makes this an easy option.

And what do you want? What do you like about the video? What do you want to change? How does it compare to that picture in your mind of what joyful heeling looks like? Keep these in mind as you move through your heelwork training and work through the exercises.

Notes:

_____

_____

_____

_____

_____

_____

_____

_____

_____

_____

_____

_____

_____

_____

_____

_____

_____

_____

CHAPTER 3:
Preparing Your Dog's Body

You've been sitting in a chair for hours. Arms and shoulders hunched over the keyboard. Your head and neck are held up at an odd angle so that your glasses hit the screen at just the right point, so you can actually see what's on it. And when you finally get up your body protests. Muscles are tight and stiff, and while it feels good to stretch, your range of motion is limited and uncomfortable. Then someone wants you to do the splits and maybe some toe touches. Even for those of you in great shape, it would be hard... and uncomfortable.

Compare that to how your body feels after a brisk walk. Blood is flowing, fresh air enters your lungs, your mind clears and your body not only cooperates but pushes you forward. When combined with a stretching regimen, our muscles loosen, become relaxed and flexible, and our movement becomes fluid and more agile. Those toe touches aren't so hard after all.

Preparing your dog's body with both some warm-up before heelwork and some physical conditioning over the long run will help your dog be more comfortable in their movement. Without that, it's difficult to feel joy. It's important that our dogs' bodies are prepared for what we are asking of them of them. Heeling itself is not the best warm-up, though a bit of trotting to loosen muscles and get air in the lungs and blood flowing can be a valued part of a warm-up.

Heelwork is physically demanding.

When you compare a visual of a dog naturally trotting, it looks very little like the picture we have in our head of a flashy heel. The head carriage, chest, and forelegs all look different. Both are beautiful, and very different.

Your picture of beautiful heelwork may not be exactly like those above, but they show the strong contrast between what we are trying to draw out of the dog and the dog's natural movement. No wonder it's so hard! No wonder we need to make this fun for our dogs!

Below are exercises to assess and increase your dog's physical ability to give you what you want. I am not an expert in canine conditioning. These are exercises I have learned from those who are! It's important they are done correctly and that you move slowly. I highly recommend that you seek out the advice of an experienced professional in the field of canine conditioning, especially if your dog is showing any resistance to any of the exercises.

Before stretching be sure to warm your dog's muscles so they are more pliable. A few minutes of brisk walking or chasing tossed treats is usually sufficient to warm your dog up for stretches.

Cookie Stretches for Neck, Back, and Push from the Rear

Stretching can increase range of motion and maintain flexibility. That means our dogs won't be feeling discomfort when we ask them for certain criteria, such as head up or forelegs lifted. Cookie stretches are just that! We are not teaching behaviors here but rather motivating the dog through luring and generous rewards for putting out the effort. Though for many dogs, marking the stretch with a clicker can maintain motivation for additional reps. In general 3-6 reps is sufficient in a session.

Step 1: Ask your dog to put their front feet on a chair or stool. The surface you'll ask your dog to put their feet on should be at about their shoulder height. Be sure the surface is not slick or slippery and that the stool or chair is stable. Your dog should feel secure when they are up there. Reward with some *Fast Food* (several treats in a row) just for being up there. Release and reset a few times with a cookie toss to ensure they offer to get back on and that we get the blood flowing a little bit.

Step 2: Using a lure close to the dog's nose, stretch their neck upward so that their neck, shoulders and back reach upward in a line. Work to keep the head straight and not turned to the side. Your hand should be up high but over their chest and not back toward their shoulders. If you reach too high with the lure, your dog will give up or try to twist their body. Your lure should stay almost touching the dog's nose.

A mirror will be beneficial, or if you are using a tablet or phone to video you may be able to see with your device in "selfie" mode.

Mark when you feel your dog has stretched upward as far as they can. If your dog struggles or moves their feet around, lower your hand. We can build up to a greater stretch. It's more important that your dog's head isn't tilting backward or twisting to get the treat, or that they aren't moving their feet a lot. The dog's head should be comfortable even if the nose is more forward rather than up.

When in doubt give the treat! Better to be super generous here for effort than to have your dog become frustrated and give up!

As the stretch becomes more comfortable and lengthened, watch your dog's hip, chest, and back rather than nose/head. Mark and reward when the hips tuck in and the chest lifts. This will stretch out the back, encourage lift and help create push from the rear for heelwork.

Compare the two photos below. Note the photo on the left, the forelegs are straight under the shoulders with the chest facing forward and the rear legs are extended with the topline and head forming a straight line from tail to nose. This is what you want your dog to work towards.

However! If your dog has physical challenges such as arthritis, hip or hock issues please take these into consideration! Some dogs may need to work this exercise from a lower height. And that's okay too! Your dog's physical health and comfort are of utmost importance! Joy doesn't happen if it hurts!

Correct alignment

Incorrect alignment

More Cookie Stretches for Neck and Back

With your dog in a stand and you facing their side, use your hand farthest from their head to reach under their belly and forward through their front legs. Allow your dog to bend their neck down to their chest to nibble at the treats in your hand. Then use your other hand with treats to bring their head level again before repeating.

Gumby Stretches for Neck, Back and Shoulders

Step 1: Start with your dog between your legs. Be sure they are comfortable there. Provide a little *Fast Food* (several treats in a row) to build value in remaining between your legs.

Step 2: Draw your dog's nose with a lure so that they wrap their head toward and in front of one of your legs. Your dog's ribs should stay in place between your legs, adjusting the wrap as necessary. Their front feet should remain in place. Allow them to nibble at the treats. Return to center and then work the other side. Alternate sides. This should be a gentle stretch of the neck and side of the dog. It also helps with flexibility of the neck, shoulders and back.

High Fives for Shoulder Stretch

High fives or paw lifts can help build flexibility in the shoulder muscles and joints. They are also freestyle foundation behaviors. There are many ways to teach a paw lift. For the purpose of stretching, you can prompt or model this until the dog is targeting your hand.

By modeling or prompting, I mean simply lifting your dog's paw, or tickling behind the stopper pad, until your hand moving toward the paw causes your dog to anticipate and offer their paw toward your hand. I use the hand directly across from the dog's paw.

Once the dog is lifting their paw, you can raise your target hand so your dog can get more of an upward reach and a little longer stretch. Listen to your dog. If they pull away or struggle, lower your hand. Remember you want to keep your dog happy here, so lots of cookies and play breaks! Don't drill this!

Take a Bow! For Shoulder Stretch

With your dog in a stand and you facing their side, use your hand closest to your dog's head to lure them forward a couple of steps. Then without pausing, move your lure toward their chest to a point on the ground between their front paws. As your dog starts to rock back to get to the treat, mark and reward.

Shape the depth of the bow, or how close their chest comes to the ground, by marking and rewarding small increments of the bend in their elbow. Some dogs will have more stretch in the shoulders while others will have more stretch in the back. If your dog lays down during this process you can lure them back into the stand and start over or toss the treat forward to bring them out of the down. Avoid feeding in the down.

V-Target for Neck Strength

The V-target is similar to the sustained nose-to-hand target. I like my hand target to be single and fast – a touch and go - for a mark and reward then ready for another, so I generally don't teach a sustained hand target. I do want a way to reinforce and build value and strength in my dog's ability to keep their head up for longer periods of time though and that's where the V-target comes in.

Step 1: Make a V with your index and middle finger, pointing down toward the floor. This will act as a cradle or bridge for your dog to place their muzzle.

Step 2: Shape your dog to move into the V and then to lift their muzzle upward into the V of your fingers. Use a treat toss to reset.

If your dog struggles with the shaping aspect of this, you can provide a lure between your fingers for a few reps to jump-start this.

Step 3: When your dog is predictably sliding into the V, start to withhold your marker for a little more pressure into your hand as your dog pushes upward. Then gradually add a little duration. This is a strength building and stretching exercise. Forward movement or heeling while the dog's muzzle is in the V is not a requirement to benefit from this exercise.

Stand Down Stand

With your dog's front feet on a flat or very low target, lure your dog into a fold back down. Once in the down, lure your dog up into the stand. Be sure your lure holds your dog's head level and it is not moving up or down or side to side. Help your dog create a slow and methodical movement through the movement of your lure. Providing a bit of *Fast Food* in each position provides a quick respite between repetitions as well as building value in remaining on the target.

Cavaletti

I use cavaletti to help my dogs learn how to place their feet for best balance and to help create lift and a bit of prance in their steps. For some dogs, this comes naturally, for most not so much. Don't be surprised if your dog struggles with this a little. Some will be re-learning how to move.

I don't recommend using a lure in your hand to lead your dog. If your dog is new to cavaletti, you can place treats, a kind of "Hansel and Gretel" trail for them to **walk** through a couple of times. Don't stay at this level long as we don't really want the dog to dip their head in search of treats.

Placing a target at the end to prompt them to go through will help prevent them from turning in toward you at the end. Tossed treats can build too much speed. The Hansel and Gretel method can help slow down rushing for a dog that tends to jump. I usually just walk alongside or slightly ahead of my dog. You may have to experiment to see what works best for your dog.

The **distance** between the bars to start should be about the height of your dog at the withers or top of their shoulders. This should make for an easy gait for your dog. You may have to adjust a bit. Start with the **height** at about your dog's wrist, or lower if your dog has never done cavaletti before.

To get higher leg lifts, raise the height slightly and gradually, to somewhere between the wrist and elbow of the dog's forearm. The bars should never go above your dog's elbow. You will likely need to bring the distance in just a little closer as well, as your dog will need to collect his gait to be able to move through the slightly higher poles. Have your dog walk initially rather than trot. As they learn where and how to place their feet, they will be able to start to trot.

You'll want to experiment a little with the distance and height depending on your dog's structure and know that your dog will need some time to adjust and work out what feels right for them. Don't give up too soon on a particular height or distance. It will take your dog several times through to find their rhythm. If they are struggling to find a rhythm, lessen the difficulty by lowering the height or adjusting the distance between bars.

Once your dog finds their rhythm with the higher bar setting, and has practiced a couple of sessions, lower the bars back down **within the same session**. You should see an increase in how high they are lifting their legs. Alternating the height of bars between higher and lower will help maintain that bit of a lift of the paws and legs.

> ### Make Your Own Cavaletti
>
> *Make your own cavaletti using wind-proof cones (collapsible cones with holes in them available at sports stores or online) and PVC pipe found at hardware or home improvement stores.*
>
> *You can also use two sets of training gates set up in parallel rows (see training gates in section on training aids and props). Place PVC poles through the training gate corridor at regular intervals according to your dog's height and stride. Allow poles to "break away" by not extending ends too far through the training gates. A benefit of the training gate is that it is easy to set bar height and spacing.*
>
> *AffordableAgility.com also has a cool adjustable cavaletti set that changes height by turning them on their "legs"*
>
> **affordableagility.com/cavaletti**

Be sure to provide adequate rewards. This is an important part of your conditioning exercises. This is hard work, so pay well and pay frequently! Give plenty of play breaks between sets of 3 or 4 passes. Provide lots of rewards for each pass. Repeat no more than 2 or 3 sets of 3 or 4 passes and maybe less depending on your dog's age, structure, and comfort of the exercise.

You can mix your bar height. Have your first 3 bars in the pass be at the high height, and your second 3 at the lower height. Mark when you see the same lift your dog gave in the first half with the high bars as they are going over the lower bars.

You can also alternate the bar height: high, low, high, low.

As your dog's sessions become consistent and they continue to build a rhythm and ease of movement, watch your dog's feet as they come out of the cavaletti and mark those bits of higher leg lift when there are no bars left and they are still moving forward.

Keeping your dog moving straight all the way through the bars is important. Having a target they can move to will prevent them from turning toward you as they come out of the cavaletti, and allow you to stand where you have a good view of them from the side.

Don't expect your dog to maintain a prancing trot without the bars as a reminder right away! This takes time for your dog to build the muscles and patterning to trot with a little prance. We'll be introducing more exercises that also reinforce that bit of collection that we are working toward with the cavaletti.

Frequency of Conditioning Exercises

How frequently you work these exercises depends on your dog's condition to start with. If your dog isn't used to any kind of conditioning program you don't want to do a lot of repetitions or add difficulty when you first begin. Think of how we as humans might structure an exercise program - no marathons to start.

Three to Four times a week at an intensity suitable for your dog's current physical condition is reasonable. However only a couple of times a week may not get you the desired result.

When you do your stretches, (such as the cookie stretches or paw lift stretches), you will be able to "feel" if the dog is straining on the paw lifts. Or if the dog is lifting feet or twisting or hopping on the cookie stretches, then it's too hard. Find where the dog is comfortable, then gradually you'll be able to ask for a little more stretch.

As you work through the different exercises some may be familiar, others maybe not. Don't feel that you have to do them all. Some are a progression meant to be worked over time. Don't rush! This isn't a race. It's a means of building a physical skill and that can take time.

Just like us, in our own exercise and conditioning, we want to gradually increase our body's ability to do more. The term "doable difficulty" should be kept in mind.

And remember, video is your friend. It will show you whether your dog is accepting of the level you are asking.

Notes:

PART II

Let The Games Begin

"A game is a form of play with structure and goals."
— Kevin Maroney

CHAPTER 4:

Construct Games

Construct games are those activities that can be used alone or in combination to create broader games, build skills and motivation, and can be used as either primary or secondary reinforcement. The enjoyment and reinforcement of the construct games help to classically condition our dogs to find joy in the heeling games.

There are several games that can be combined and used in different ways. The behaviors below are used in many of the games and exercises. Your dog's understanding, fluency and enjoyment of these games will greatly enhance their enjoyment and success at other games and more importantly in your heelwork. For me, these construct games are critical for building enjoyment and value in heeling:

- 🐾 Hand Target
- 🐾 Jump to Food
- 🐾 Chase Food
- 🐾 Around a Cone

Take the time to build value and create energy and enjoyment in these before starting to combine them or use them in the heeling games.

There are specific mechanics involved with each that you will learn here. That's important to note. You may already use some of these games in your training, though you may need to adjust your application or presentation slightly to fit within the games presented in this book.

Shaping a Clean Hand Target

There are several different ways that the hand target, which is your dog pushing their nose into the flat palm of your hand, can be used. Not all trainers use it the same way, so you'll want to read carefully how it will be used in this program.

The hand touch, or target, plays a major role in almost all of my training. It acts as a secondary reinforcer, a passive lure, and a target and is not only used in a variety of games but also helps to build duration in your heelwork. It brings an instant connection. My dog is physically and emotionally connected to me, and me to them. With its strong history of reward, a hand touch becomes a fun activity that acts as a secondary reinforcer, benefiting whatever behavior precedes it.

We'll be using what I refer to as a "touch and treat," nose-to-hand-target, rather than a sustained nose-to-hand-target. Every touch earns reinforcement, just as every click or other marker earns reinforcement. While the sustained nose-to-hand target can have value, for our purpose of finding joy in heeling we'll be using the touch and treat, as not only part of the games and reinforcement, but as a way of teaching duration without the aid of the sustained hand target.

No verbal cue will be used to tell the dog to touch your hand. The way you present your hand will become a cue. Make your presentation distinct. While many handlers choose to use an open palm as their target surface, you can also teach this using a two-finger touch, with just two fingers extended. The two-finger option is great for small or toy breeds.

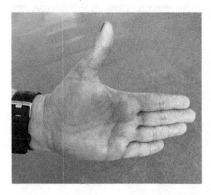

Even if you feel you have a strong hand touch, going through these steps can only benefit your dog's understanding and value.

Step 1: Present your hand out away from you and to your side. Keep your fingers close together and try to hyper-extend your palm. Be sure your hand is low enough that your dog can get to it easily. For small dogs, I like to start this sitting on the floor.

Keep your hand still or moving away from your dog slightly, rather than into your dog. A hand moving toward your dog's face can cause them to back away or be tentative in moving forward to touch your hand. We want your hand target to be something your dog drives toward and finds value in.

Mark when your dog looks at or moves toward your hand, then toss your treat a few feet away.

After you mark, be sure to pause, about the time it takes you to take a breath, before reaching for your pocket or bait bag. Your marker should be separated from the start of your treat delivery and that includes reaching for your treat. We want your dog focused on touching your hand and not glancing at your pocket. Using the same hand the dog touches to get your treat will help to separate your marker from reaching for a reward. This separation between marking the behavior and reinforcing the behavior is one of the skills that aid in clean training and clear communication.

Step 2: Repeat for a few repetitions, gradually increasing your dog's proximity to your hand until they lightly touch it with their nose.

Providing a reset toss can provide the little bit of distance needed for your dog to see and approach your hand. However, providing a treat closer to your hand will help to create more reps in a shorter time, and close the time between reinforcements. This tighter loop can also prevent any extraneous behavior such as sniffing between reps. You will likely use both of these methods (reset toss, or tight loop) at various times in your training.

As you continue, start to select for more pressure on your hand. You might be tempted to help your dog by moving your hand closer to them. Resist this urge! You want them to reach toward your hand instead.

Removing your hand between repetitions, by hiding it behind your back or at your side, will add some anticipation for the dog and result in them looking forward to continuing the game.

Step 3: Start to select for the more deliberate and finally the "pushy" touches. You really want your dog driving into your hand. If they are tentative after a few touches, review your video. It could be that you aren't aware of a slight forward movement in your hand. Or you might need to raise the value of your reward.

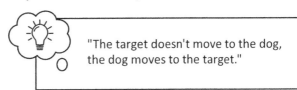
"The target doesn't move to the dog, the dog moves to the target."

Be sure to reward the hand touch on a 1:1 ratio. You want to build and maintain a high degree of value for the hand target to be of use to you.

Step 4: Once your dog is deliberately and joyfully moving toward and touching your hand, you can start to add a little more action - change hands, bring it a little higher. Will your dog jump a little to get to it? Will your dog chase it a little if it moves away? Will they move through your legs to get to it? Have fun with your hand targets! They are part of what will bring joy to your heelwork!

Jump to Food

It may surprise you that some dogs struggle with jumping up for food! This can be due to previous learning, or it can be that the dog really doesn't know how to physically jump in a way that they can target the food accurately.

Start in a stationary, standing position with your dog in front of you. Encourage your dog to come up off their front feet to take a food treat. Your dog's rear feet should remain on the ground. Some dogs will need a release cue (such as "okay") or other cue that

Test Your Hand Target! Tug to Touch:

Having a strong desire in your dog to get to and touch your hand will greatly increase your success at the games and exercises.

When your hand is the only option, then it's an easy choice for your dog. What if your dog has to choose between your hand and a tug or other toy? What about a treat? We can build greater value in the hand target by reinforcing the touch by giving access to the tug, toy, treat or other desired item.

After warming up with a few reps of hand touch for rewards, rather than removing access to the reward (treat, toy or tug), continue to hold it in your other hand as you present your target hand for your dog to touch. You may have to place your target hand a bit closer to your dog.

As soon as your dog releases the tug or toy and touches your hand, mark and reward with the tug/toy.

If you are using food for this exercise, you can leave your food in an open hand. Present both an open hand with food and your hand target. If your dog moves to the food, close your hand, and make the choice of touching your target hand more obvious. Start with lower value food and work up to higher value.

If your dog struggles with this game and you feel you have a lot of value in your touch behavior, lower the level of value of the competing attraction or lessen the intensity or the time tugging before presenting your hand. You could try using a less favored toy or maybe food instead, or food in a pile at a distance. There is always something we can change - either by raising the value of reward for the touch, or lowering the value of the dog's options.

Not quite ready for the challenge? Go back to building value in the touch without the added difficulty.

gives them permission to take the food, (such as "get it"). Be sure your food isn't too high to start. Reward any effort by giving them the food. Gradually increase your criteria until they are confidently jumping up several inches to get the food. Repeat with your dog at your side.

If your dog is reluctant to jump up to get to the food, you can use a stool or chair as a transition. This allows them to get the treat without having to jump up to start.

Standing with the stool between you and your dog, and holding a treat over the stool, encourage them to put their front feet up on the stool to get the treat. In subsequent reps, gradually start to hold the food farther out in front of you on the other side of the stool so that they are able to get the treat with their front feet free in the air and not touching the stool. Mark and reward your dog bringing his front feet off the ground and not for touching the stool. You can then remove the stool. Your dog should be more willing to jump to get the food held in front of you.

Chase Food - Food Bowling

Many of you probably already use *Food Bowling* or chasing food in your training to relieve pressure, enhance reinforcement, set up for the next repetition, or give you and your dog a break. Because we'll be using *Food Bowling* in some of the games we'll be playing, I want to make sure to cover the basics here and talk about technique. While chasing food is a dog skill, bowling food is a handler skill.

Make sure the treat is large enough and of a color that contrasts with the surface on which you are bowling. Make sure your treats don't stick to each other or crumble apart. You want to be able to get a single treat out and not have several treats go flying.

Flat, harder surfaces are best, but grass can work if the treats are large enough to be visible (but not so large that your dog has to chew or gets full quickly).

Stand in the center of the area you will be using. Your dog will be moving away from you, then back toward you, and away from you again. You will be pivoting, or turning in the direction you will be bowling the treat.

Bowl your food across your body and forward as you turn your back to your dog. You want your back to be a part of the cue for the dog to move toward you. As your dog moves back to you from getting the treat, and after turning 180 degrees away from your dog, bowl another treat in the new direction. Always use the hand that is closest to the side the dog passes you on. If your dog is passing you on the left, use your left hand to bowl.

Think of the treat as a bowling ball. It's heavy! You don't want to backhand it or lob it. Be sure to follow through just as you would a bowling ball headed to the pins.

It's a good idea to practice bowling without your dog. If your treat is flying through the air higher than your waist then bowl lower. Following through with your arm gives your dog a direction to move to get to the treat. The goal is that the treat is low to the ground and rolls and isn't lobbed into the air.

An important goal here is continual motion in your dog. We don't want them to run up to you, stop, then go chase the treat. You want to bowl the next treat as they are moving to you so they are in continual motion. The reason for this will become apparent as we add it to your heelwork.

You can use cues if you want: "get it", "come" or your dog's name, and "get it."

Two-Toy Game

You may be wondering If you can use toys in place of food when an exercise calls for *Food Bowling*. The short answer is yes! The complete answer is a little more complicated.

When *Food Bowling* is called for in an exercise, there may be several reasons for it. In most cases its purpose is two-fold. It acts as reinforcement and as a respite or relief from pressure, pushing the dog way from the handler. Toys can fill both purposes.

Other times, *Food Bowling* serves a more functional purpose within a larger game or exercise. If you want to use toys within these exercises then the mechanics are a little more complex. And there are some prerequisite skills that you and your dog should have. In most cases, you will want to use two identical toys.

Your dog should be able to reliably drop the toy at your feet, or at the presentation of another toy. Being able to drop the toy at the presentation of another toy allows for continual motion, as in the *Food Bowling* game. When the second toy is presented, the dog drops the first toy and continues moving forward in chase of the newly thrown toy.

When we start to combine games and add in our heeling criteria, the handler should be able to quickly tuck the toy away, out of sight, and be ready to move into the next element of the game or exercise. So while you do want to use toys as part of your reinforcement or reward event, you will want to take these mechanics and prerequisites into consideration when using toys in place of *Food Bowling*.

Out and Around a Cone

There are several ways to teach a dog to move ahead of you and go around a cone. If your goal is to teach both left and right side heeling, you will want to teach your dog to go around the cone both clockwise and counter-clockwise.

You can use luring, shaping, or structured shaping.

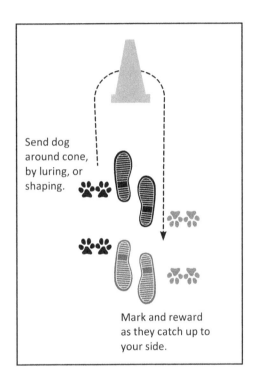

Send dog around cone, by luring, or shaping.

Mark and reward as they catch up to your side.

When luring your dog to go around a cone, start close, with your dog on your left side for teaching clockwise or on your right for teaching counter-clockwise.

With your leg closest to your dog, step forward as you lure (or use a hand signal) to encourage your dog around the cone. Mark as your dog rounds the cone, then turn so you and your dog are now facing the same direction with your back to the cone. Feed as they come alongside you.

As you repeat this, remove the food from your lure hand and transfer to a hand cue. Once transferred to a hand cue you can start to add small increments of distance from the cone until you are about 6 feet from the cone. You can then add your verbal cue, by inserting it just before your hand cue.

If shaping the dog to go around a cone, start close, about two to three feet from the cone. Have your dog in the general vicinity of your left side if you want them to go clockwise, and your right side if you want them to go counter-clockwise.

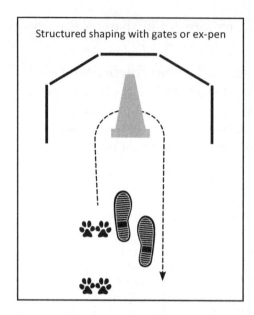

Structured shaping with gates or ex-pen

Initially, mark and reward any interest in the cone including looking at or stepping toward the cone. You can toss your treat near where your dog started, or have your dog come back to you to take the treat from your hand.

Gradually increase your criteria and the timing of your marker to when the dog is at "the point of no return" or the three-quarter point of going around the cone. Turn in the same direction as your dog and bowl your treat a short distance to reset them for the next repetition.

You can also opt to use "structured shaping" to teach your dog to go around the cone. In structured shaping, you can use a prop, such as an ex-pen or set of training gates to make the dog's path obvious by placing the barrier in the shape of a semi-circle around your cone, with enough space for the dog to maneuver all the way around the cone.

Notes:

CHAPTER 5:
Combining the Construct Games for More Joy!

Many of the games can and should be combined to create more joy and greater reinforcement value. These games don't just create our criteria of energy, lift, and animation, but act as reward events. It's the value you build into the game that creates the emotional response that we want to attach to your heelwork.

The longer and harder your dog works, the longer your reward event, with the greatest level of joy! Combining the games – any of the games outlined in this book – as well as some of your own, allows for plenty of opportunities to associate heeling with fun activities. They act as reinforcement for the exercises that involve more precision and accuracy. By layering the games within the precision and accuracy exercises, heeling becomes an integral part of the fun and joy. Heeling predicts games and games predict heeling!

Your hand target is a fundamental part of many of the exercises and games. We will start to refine our criteria, and mark not only the hand touch, but also that offered lift created from the anticipation and expectation of the hand being presented.

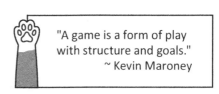

"A game is a form of play with structure and goals."
~ Kevin Maroney

Jump for Joy! Lift and Driving from the Rear

When we think about energetic and flashy heeling, the picture often includes a lifted chest and the weight shifting to the rear to accentuate a lightness and prance of the front legs. Through the use of *Jump to Hand/Jump to Food* skills (which I'll often refer to as *Jump for Joy*) the dog will learn to shift their weight, drive from the rear and lift their head and chest.

To encourage your dog to push from their rear and bring their front feet off the ground, we'll be using your newly taught skills of the hand touch and jump for food. These are the *Jump for Joy* games.

These *Jump for Joy* games allow us to create, mark and reward the dog for lifting their head and chest, shifting their weight to their rear and lightening the load on the front.

How to Play the Game:

Step 1: Encourage your dog to move with you as you take steps backward. Smile! Give your dog something to look at! Say sweet things! Then offer a treat just over their head and encourage them to jump to get it. You may need to pause your movement for your dog to be able to jump up toward the food.

This shouldn't be a high leap, but rather just enough jump to bring the front feet off the ground several inches. We want the dog pushing up from the rear. Their rear feet should stay firmly on the ground. If you have taught your dog to jump to food previously, they should catch on quickly.

Step 2: Add a change of position. Have your dog jump to food with you moving backward still, but your dog in a "reverse heel" position with their head at your side rather than directly in front of you.

Step 3: After a few repetitions, you can start to move forward, with your dog at your side, also moving forward. Present your food at your side near your hip - the height is dependent on your dog - and encourage your dog to jump a bit to get it.

Some dogs will need you to pause or stop to allow them to jump to get to the food. Other dogs become adept at jumping to the food while in movement. Either way, once the dog gets the food, you will want to stop to allow them to enjoy their reward.

Don't worry just yet about whether your dog is in a precise or accurate heel position. Right now, we just want them in the game of *Jump to Food*.

Step 4: When you and your dog are comfortable with the mechanics of jumping to food, you can then work through the same steps using a hand target for the *Jump to Hand* game.

Your hand target is used in a very specific location: At your side just above where you want your dog's head to be while in heel position. Your palm should be facing down and almost parallel to the ground and angled very slightly toward you, so your dog can move a bit under it before coming up to touch. Initially, mark as your dog lifts up and touches your hand, then follow up with having them *Jump to Food*.

As you continue to play the games that include *Jump to Hand* it's okay if sometimes you are marking the hand touch, and sometimes you are marking the jump *to* the hand, and sometimes you may be marking the lift or animation in anticipation, even before the hand has been presented (in which case the presentation of your hand can act as the marker). Any and all are fine as each creates the same result, reinforcement for lift, animation and driving from the rear.

Momentum and Collection

From the previous chapter, the higher cavaletti bars help our dogs learn to pick up their feet, creating a bit of lift. The raised bar and shorter distance between the bars require that they collect their energy upward rather than extend forward.

When a dog extends their movement, the limbs stretch forward. When they collect their movement, the dog's stride shortens and their legs come upward, creating the appearance of lift. Changing a dog's speed with some abruptness can also create collection, providing another opportunity to mark and reward that appearance of animation and lift. The next few games do just that!

Combining Food Bowling and Jump for Joy

In this game, your dog will start to learn that moving into and then moving while in heel position is super fun, exciting and results in not only a reward but in starting the game again. This is an active, in motion game with few stops. You will be associating some of your dog's favorite activities – running, chasing food, and jumping – with coming alongside you and eventually seeking out heel position.

"Harry is way more determined to come into heel and I love his looking up to me expecting the hand touch."
~ Chiho and Harry

This game also causes the dog to collect their forward energy and shift it upward, giving you an opportunity to mark for not only position or proximity but the accompanying energy resulting from the game. .

This, and the other construct game combinations are just the beginning of shaping animated heelwork.

How to Play the Game:

Step 1: Start with a game of *Food Bowling* by bowling your treat forward in one direction, and then as your dog starts moving back to you, turn your back to your dog to bowl in the other direction. Remember you don't want them to stop, but to run past you to get to the bowled treat. So time your treat bowling accordingly.

Step 2: After a few tosses and turns, as your dog moves back to you in anticipation of another bowled treat, turn away and start walking forward briskly. As your dog catches up to you, present your hand near your hip about where you would want their head to be while heeling. Keep your arm close to your body with your elbow firm against your side. When they touch your palm with their nose, mark, take a couple of extra steps as you get your treat out, and reward with a *Jump to Food*. Be sure to maintain your close in arm position.

If your dog struggles when jumping to your hand, you may want to start with having them jump to a piece of food instead. Then work to strengthen the hand touch outside of this game.

Step 3: After your dog has finished their reward, bowl another piece of food forward to start the game again.

Step 4: Gradually you will be able to start to extend and then vary the number of steps your dog remains alongside you before presenting your hand to touch and following up with a *Jump to Food*. Sometimes you will present your hand right away, and sometimes after a few steps or more!

As you continue to play this game, your dog will start to show you signs of anticipation of your hand appearing. They will start to lift their chest and head a little. Mark that, even before you present your hand! Your marker will tell them why they are getting the reward and they will start to work to maintain that lift.

Ideally, you will catch moments of the lift before your hand is presented, and be able to mark. Other times you will present your hand and mark and reward the touch. This little bit of animation and engagement of "Will they show their hand? Will they not show their hand?" creates a bit of a bounce and lift in your dog's step. And the fast-paced action of getting to chase food not only starts the game again but provides a little respite from the close-in position you are working toward.

Combining Out and Around a Cone with Food Bowling

This game is super fun for many dogs. It's similar to straight *Food Bowling* but instead of bowling your food in both directions, you will send your dog around the cone in one direction, then as they round the cone, turn and bowl your food in the other direction. Just as in combining *Food Bowling* and *Jump for Joy*, our goal is to build speed as they move toward and then past us to chase the food.

How to Play the Game:

Step 1: Start about 6-10 feet from the cone, depending on the size and skill of your dog – closer for smaller dogs or dogs that do not yet have distance in being able to go around the cone.

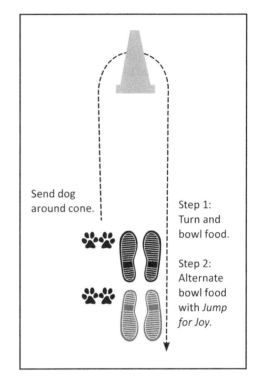

Send dog around cone.

Step 1: Turn and bowl food.

Step 2: Alternate bowl food with *Jump for Joy*.

If you are working your left side heel, you want your dog to go clockwise around the cone, starting with them on your left side. If you are working your right side heel, you want your dog to go counter-clockwise around the cone, starting with them on your right side.

Step 2: Use your hand closest to your dog to send them out and around the cone, or you can use a verbal cue. As they round the cone, turn 180 degrees in the same direction (clockwise if your dog is going clockwise around the cone and counter-clockwise if your dog is moving counter-clockwise around the cone) and use the same hand, closest to the dog, to now bowl the treat so they run past you to get to the treat.

Step 3: After bowling the treat for the dog to chase, continue to turn in the same direction continuing in another 180-degree turn. Look over your shoulder on the side you want the dog to come up on (left for left, right for right) then send them around the cone again for another game of *Food Bowling*.

As your dog is rewarded with a game of chasing bowled food each time they go around the cone, you will be able to add a little more distance between you and the cone. Work toward 10-12 feet of distance.

The goal is that the dog moves continuously from the cone to the bowled treat and back past you and around the cone again - no stops and starts – but rather a continuous loop. Movement creates joy!

Bowling the food also creates speed, which is important when we use this game for collection in the next game.

This also makes a great game to relieve the pressure that can build up when we ask our dogs to heel for longer stretches. Intermittently sending your dog out around a well-placed cone during heeling allows you to continue to build your duration while keeping it fun.

Catch Me If You Cone

This game combines *Out and Around a Cone/Food Bowling* with *Jump for Joy*.

How to Play the Game:

Step 1: Start with a quick game of *Out and Around a Cone/Food Bowling*. Be sure you are turning in the same direction as the dog and bowling with the hand closest to the dog.

Step 2: After a few repetitions, once your dog is expecting a treat will be bowled in the direction they are moving, add your *Jump for Joy* game. As they round the cone, turn away from your dog taking several steps forward. As your dog moves toward you and comes alongside you, present your *Jump to Hand* target and reward with *Jump to Food*.

As with the previous *Food Bowling* and *Jump for Joy* game, your dog will start to collect their energy to prepare their body to jump to the hand.

As you continue, your dog will start to anticipate the appearance of your hand. That abrupt slowing and collection will carry the energy upward and you may be able to see and mark that lift even before you present your hand. Don't wait for it, just watch for it. Still present your hand, even if you mark. After you mark, continue to move forward a couple of steps as you get your food out, and then provide your primary reinforcement with a *Jump to Food*. You can then stop to allow your dog to enjoy their reward before starting the game again with either *Food Bowling* or sending *Out and Around the Cone*.

Ideally, your dog is in a gallop or fast trot when they catch up to you. If they are dropping into a slow trot or fast walk, start closer to the cone and do a few more passes of *Food Bowling* to build speed before trying again. Increasing the value of your food can also increase speed and energy.

As you play the game over time, and practice the precision games and exercises outlined later in this book, you will gradually increase the number of steps you and your dog take while they are in position before presenting your hand target. We can then build duration in position, terminating in the presentation of the hand target and *Jump to Food*.

By combining the different construct games to create new games, we not only have greater opportunities to facilitate and reinforce collection and lift, but we can also provide more enjoyment for our dogs.

An added benefit of these games is that they teach our dogs about "moving attention." In moving attention, precision and accuracy are secondary to animation and energy. Without focus and attention, our heeling will appear dull and lackluster despite great positioning. The active nature of these games encourages your dog to be attentive and focused with a willingness to engage. This will carry over when we move into more precision and accuracy exercises.

Help! My Dog Won't Stop Jumping Now!

Occasionally I'll see a dog that has so much value in the Jump for Joy *exercises that he seems to be on a pogo stick while heeling! While continually jumping when heeling is not desirable, we have been reinforcing the dog for just that behavior. Anything that we reinforce will increase. Our dog is likely to offer behaviors that are heavily reinforced. The purpose of the* Jump for Joy *exercises is to increase offered upward energy. There are times, though, when a strong reinforcement history can get us more than what we want.*

A dog that might over-rotate on pivots, or sit every time they move to heel, or get on a platform as soon as it's available, likely developed their behavior due to an abundance of reinforcement. Behavior increases through our rate of reward and can be decreased by reinforcing the alternative, more desirable behavior.

So if your dog has taken to jumping jacks, decrease the Jump to Hand *and discontinue* Jump to Food *for a while. While heeling, mark, and increase your reinforcement for four on the floor by placing your reward low, even on the ground. We can change behavior fairly quickly by making small changes in what and where we reinforce.*

CHAPTER 6:
Attention, Focus and Engagement: What's the Difference?

These three terms are often used interchangeably. I think of them each as having different criteria. Each can be trained separately, though they ideally come together in practice. I define them as:

Attention: Looking at the handler – preferably face or eyes. This doesn't always mean what it looks like! Your dog may be looking at you and still be unable to engage or respond to cues! However, your dog looking at you is an indication they are connected to you in some way. For me, it gives me a level of confidence that my dog is ready to focus and engage.

Focus: Purposeful attention on the task or cue with strong intention. This involves concentration and readiness to respond. When a dog is focused, they can shut out extraneous stimuli that can interfere with their ability to respond.

Engagement: Actively involved with the handler, and fully present. In general, if you have engagement, you have attention and focus, though not always. Arousal can be a factor that limits both focus and attention.

Ideally, all three are present and our dog's level of arousal, animation, and emotions are in a place of learning and enjoyment.

Attention and Focus Games

In many cases, our heeling falls apart, not because our dogs don't know how to heel but because they don't know how to ignore external stimuli and maintain focus and attention. This inability to maintain focus and attention can spiral into worry and a lack of confidence. There is no joy without confidence. We want our dogs to think of environmental distractions as part of the game! We want the added difficulty to become the cue to maintain focus and look to you.

Teaching eye contact as a behavior will greatly encourage the head up posture that many of us want. Too often, I think handlers assume that attention and eye contact will be offered by the dog as a part of training. While for many that's true, for just as many it's not! Training eye contact as a behavior allows you to split it out from the rest of your training and provide a higher rate of reward as well as additional criteria such as increasing duration and working in distracting settings.

30-Second Game

While I *do* want my dog to offer eye contact, I also like to have a support cue. My verbal cue for eye contact is "ready?" I expect to see a response when I give that cue. If I want the response though, I need to teach my dog the meaning of the word. The 30-Second Game teaches the dog a cue for eye contact and also reinforces offered attention at a very high rate.

This game has 3 parts. Each part lasts 30 seconds, for a total of 90 seconds in a sessions. In the first part, you will create a cue for eye contact. It can be a verbal cue or a physical cue. In the second part, the dog will be rewarded for offering eye contact. And in the third part, the dog will be rewarded for a small amount (2-4 seconds) of duration.

How To Play the Game:

Your dog can be sitting or standing, their choice. Most dogs opt to sit. You can also work this in various positions in relation to your body, though I would start in front of you.

Step 1: Set your timer for 30 seconds. Give a cue that you want to mean eye contact – support it with a hand cue up to your face to ensure that your dog actually looks up at you. As soon as your dog brings their eyes up to your face, mark and reward. Don't wait! You want to mark and reward a glance up to your face. The goal is to get as many "glances" as you can in 30 seconds. With practice, most dogs will be able to look to your face 6-8 times in the 30-second time frame.

Step 2: When your timer rings, set it for another 30 seconds. This time, wait for offered eye contact with no cue. When your dog glances up to your face, mark and reward. Again, no duration. A glance up earns a mark and reward – again, the goal is to get as many "glances" as you can in 30 seconds.

Step 3: In the last 30 seconds start to require 2 to 3 seconds of eye contact before you mark and reward. You may accept offered or cued eye contact. If the dog struggles with a little bit of duration go back to Steps 1 and 2.

Basic Game of "Doggy Zen"

Many of us have played what are often referred to as *Doggy Zen* or choice games, where the dog makes a choice between looking at the thing they want (food or toy) or looking at their handler's face. Often these games are taught early on in our dog's training as either "leave it" games or distraction games. These kinds of games can help to build value in eye contact as well as turn attractions/distractions into cues to look to you.

How to Play the Game:

Step 1: Hold your arms outstretched to your side at about shoulder height, with food in each hand. Keep your palms up and your hand closed. Your dog will initially want to look at your hands. Watch for, and mark and reward any glance toward your face.

Step 2: When your dog offers eye contact – just a quick glance, mark and reward. Be sure to pause slightly after you mark before bringing the food down to your dog as reward.

Overlapping your marker with your delivery can create "eye flicks" toward your hands rather than maintain eye contact as you build duration. These eye flicks can make timing your marker difficult and building duration more difficult. With clean mechanics, dogs catch on very quickly. They learn that to earn the reward they need to look at your face until you mark.

Step 3: This is a great game that has many layers. Too often we stop playing this game once our dog shows some proficiency, rather than adding those layers that make the task more challenging - layers such as duration, moving our hands, or bringing our hands lower, opening our hands, placing a pile on the floor or other added difficulty.

You can work the game in the same way using toys – in the hand, with duration, moving the toy, lowering the toy, on the floor. As you continue increasing the doable

"Ensuring your marker is distinct and separate from the delivery of your reward allows your dog to stay focused on your face until they hear the marker."

difficulty your dog will continue to learn that your face is the place! That ignoring what it is they want and looking to you is the key to getting reward.

If we stop playing these kinds of games, or if we don't continue to make the task a bit more challenging, we aren't taking full advantage of what this cool game has to offer. Adding in difficulty systematically can help develop an understanding of distraction as the cue to look to you.

Eye Flicks! Are They Okay?

It's not unusual when adding difficulty via distractions/attractions to our training to see "eye flicks", or the dog quickly glancing at whatever is splitting their focus. This occurs most frequently when we are seeing some good success and start to push the envelope a bit, moving our dog closer to the distraction/attraction or increasing the intensity of the distraction/attraction!

When you see eye flicks, avoid adding difficulty or getting closer to the distraction just yet. Stay at the same distance or intensity until those eye flicks subside to nothing then consider increasing the difficulty by moving closer or making the distraction more intense.

The goal is always continued reinforcement for maintaining eye contact (even at a bit more distance from the attraction) rather than reinforcement for the look away then look back. While it's fine to reinforce the choice to look back to you, you want to set up your level of difficulty so that it doesn't happen often. That the ratio of reward for maintaining, to reward for regaining eye contact, is closer to 10:1 than 5:1.

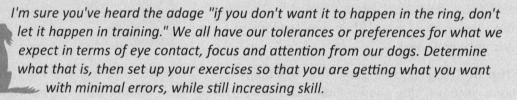

I'm sure you've heard the adage "if you don't want it to happen in the ring, don't let it happen in training." We all have our tolerances or preferences for what we expect in terms of eye contact, focus and attention from our dogs. Determine what that is, then set up your exercises so that you are getting what you want with minimal errors, while still increasing skill.

Find my Face!

For this game, the only thing your dog must do to earn a reward is to find your face. There is no duration required when you start this game.

How to Play the Game:

Step 1: Start by dropping a treat in front of you. Allow your dog to eat the treat and when they look up at you, mark and reward.

Step 2: After a few successful reps, drop or toss the treat, then turn away slightly, so your dog must work a little harder to find your face. Mark and reward just a glance before dropping or tossing again. Each time you can make it a little harder for the dog by turning away from them a bit more. Your dog does not need to come all the way in front of you! If they can see your face and you can see them looking at you without turning toward them, you can mark and reward.

Step 3: Find my Face...If you Can! You can add a bit of a challenge by tossing the treat several feet away as you turn away or by continuing to move a bit when your dog is almost in the right place to look up at your face. Keep your rate of reward and your dog's successes high enough to keep them in the game!

"The find my face game was fun- at first she was playing find my pocket or hands which reminded me to get my hands off my treat pockets... she caught on quick and then was hard to lose her!"

~ Janet and Miko

Be sure to make this a fun game! Smile! Give praise! No need to make this a boring, stick figure game! You don't need to stand in the same place. Movement can enhance the joy your dog feels when playing these games so be sure to include *Food Bowling* and maybe even a game of chase when playing this game.

If your dog is struggling, go back to the easier games of the *30-Second Game* or *Doggy Zen*.

Treats on a Seat

Most of the previous attention exercises have the handler fairly stationary. Adding movement is another way to layer difficulty in teaching your dog to remain focused on you in the presence of what we call distractions, which are actually "attractions."

In this game, we will add moving toward an attraction. Initially, precision and accuracy are secondary to remaining focused and attentive to you and the task – which is to stay by your side as you approach something the dog wants. As we move into exercises that teach position and your dog starts to understand about accuracy and precision, your dog will start to offer a more accurate and precise position, or you can add that as a later criterion.

How to Play the Game:

Step 1: With your dog on a short leash, place 3 treats on the seat of a chair. Allow your dog to see you placing the treats but prevent them from moving forward to get the treats. I don't use a "leave it" cue or stay, for this or even a cued station behavior like sit. Your dog should already have some impulse control experience in the form of other choice games before trying this. If the set-up is hard for your dog, then place the treats before you get your dog out and use a bit more distance for the exercise.

Step 2: Encourage your dog to move away from the chair with you. You can use a lure or your voice, pat your leg, or any combination to help the dog move away from the chair to a starting point where it's easy for the dog to look at you.

Step 3: Take a step or two toward the chair. Reward your dog for remaining beside you. If you use a marker, be sure it doesn't release them toward the chair. If they are unable to remain beside you, step back to a point where they can be successful. Continue to move forward toward the treats on the seat only with continued success at remaining beside you.

Step 4: Once you are within reaching distance of the seat, you can cue your dog to sit, reach forward, and one at a time give each treat to your dog. Then recall backward away from the chair for more rewards.

If your dog understands a marker as a release, you may want to avoid using that marker and opt for one that tells your dog to get reinforcement from you.

This game can be expanded to include additional criteria such as:

- Eye contact while moving to the chair
- Precise heel position while moving toward the chair
- Speed changes – moving slowly or quickly toward the chair
- Position changes at the chair
- Duration in eye contact close to the chair
- Heeling around the chair
- Recalls away from the chair with the treats still present

… your only limitation is your imagination!

Notes:

PART III

Defining the Dance

"It's the little details that are vital.
Little things make big things happen."
— John Wooden

CHAPTER 7:
Training Aids and Props: Structured Shaping

Training aids such as platforms and training gates help us to communicate criteria. They help us to define the position of "heel" to our dogs.

For many dogs, "where to be" while heeling has never been clearly explained or defined, let alone reinforced in a way that helps the dog seek it out and work to remain there.

Props, used as aids, reconcile our need for accuracy and precision with our dog's need for clarity and reinforcement. When used in conjunction with other props or aids, as in, using the different props in varying exercises to convey the same criteria, their value is compounded.

These aids also allow us to start to add the cue, as we can be certain that all criteria are being met when the prop/aid is in place. Transferring the information and criteria to the new cue is therefore a fairly streamlined process.

Props that aid in communicating criteria can have a single use or multiple uses. For example, in using platforms I use different sizes to cue my dog how to interact with them. The platforms themselves are not named with a cue. I don't give my dogs a cue to get onto the platform. The platform itself is the cue.

If the platform is large enough to stand on, then I want my dog to stand. If the

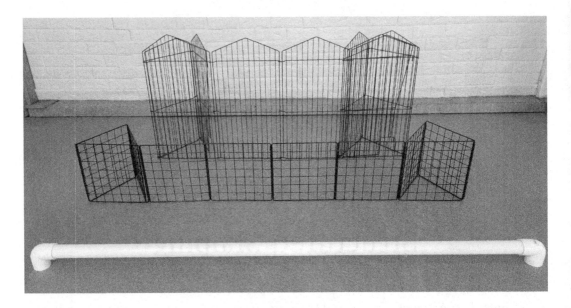

platform is only large enough to sit on, then I want my dog to sit and if the platform is only big enough to put two feet on, then I want my dog to only put two feet on.

I teach these different criteria through a high rate of reward for the correct response when getting on the various platforms. By using *Fast Food*, I can build value in the correct position when on a specific platform.

Training gates, or low barriers can be configured in different ways, and used to convey many different criteria depending on the behavior they are being used to train. When used for heelwork, in general, the gates are used to convey "straight" and "close."

In this section, we will discuss the value and uses of standing platforms, training gates, and pivot platforms, as well as visual aids for the handler. Before we get started let's talk about cues.

Consider Your Cues

Cues are not only how we label behaviors, but how we draw trained behaviors out of our dogs. Cues prompt our dogs to act. Without cues, trained behaviors are unreliable at best or at the whim of the dog at worst! Be thoughtful about what you choose as your cues and how you will use them.

"Our dogs only have so much bandwidth to concentrate on the information we are providing. Every word and movement of ours takes their focus and attention from them. Minimizing or eliminating cues we don't really need will keep them focused on the important stuff and help to prevent tiring them mentally."

It's not uncommon to have ambiguous cues for the setup and the position of heel as well as for moving in heel. In general, dogs will pick up on these cues before you even

"Props, used as aids, reconcile our need for accuracy and precision with our dog's need for clarity and reinforcement."

realize you have created a pattern in giving them. They aren't consciously given until you realize a pattern - "when I do or say this, my dog does this." There is likely some inconsistency in how or when they are provided. Despite that, our dogs tend to respond correctly much of the time.

Consider this scenario: a handler tells their dog to "heel" – meaning they want their dog to set up in a sit next to them on their left side. The dog starts to move into heel but doesn't make it all the way in. The handler then gives another cue - "get in" - and the dog pops all the way into heel and then the dog is rewarded.

I see this on a fairly regular basis. So I have to wonder what those cues mean to the dog. And further what those cues mean to the handler. Is "get in" the cue to get in position or is "heel" the cue to get in position? And consequently, is "heel" the cue to come partially into position? And how does that affect moving in heel? Or is the dog simply anticipating and sitting early because sitting is what has been reinforced?

I want my dog to learn a cue that means be at my side (different cues for left and for right heel) in a precise position in relation to my body, standing with all four feet on the floor, moving or stationary. I want them to maintain that position while I move in any direction, be it forward, backward, or into me as I move laterally. I use a single cue to mean all of those things. I build value in the position and then attach the cue.

For obedience, teaching your dog to set-up at your side in a heel position, but in a sit, is a different cue, because it's a different behavior, and the cue results in a different behavior than my "heel" cue.

So consider your cues. What do they mean to you? And have you conveyed that to your dog in a way that they understand and value?

In my experience, many handlers over-complicate cueing for heelwork. I want to simplify it for the dog (and for the handler).

There is one word for moving with me in heel position on all four as there is one thing I want my dog to understand - *no matter where my leg goes, stay with my leg.* This includes not only forward heeling, but backing in heel, sidepasses or lateral movement in heel, and pivoting in heel. The cue for all of these skills is "heel."

Pivots are a multi-functional skill that not only teaches rear end awareness, right turns, left turns, and how to find heel position but also teaches the dog your cue for moving in heel position.

Pivoting is heeling. My cue for heeling is "heel," my cue for pivots (with or without a prop) is "heel." My cue for coming into heel on the standing platform is "heel" and my cue for coming into position on all four without the platform is "heel." Sidepasses and backing in heel position is "heel." My dog is doing the exact same thing for each of those - staying in heel position while standing. "Heel" has a single definition that both my dog and I agree on. This simplifies the training for both of us.

When cueing pivots, instead of saying "pivot" or "get in," use your heel cue, as that is exactly what we want the dog to do – heel. This gives a better understanding of both the behavior and the cue. I know this is different from what you may have learned. But dog trainers know better than anyone that just because that's how it's always been done, doesn't mean that's how it should be done and that there aren't other or more effective, possibly better ways to do it.

Components of Position

Before teaching our dogs to heel we first need to define our position criteria.

If you compete in obedience or other ring sports, there is a specific definition of correct heel position. Be sure to check the rules of the sport you compete in regarding the requirements, as each sport or titling organization may have slight differences in what is considered "heel position."

If your sport of choice is musical freestyle or Rally-FrEe you determine your heel position within the requirements that the dog and the handler must overlap. That doesn't mean there is no consistent heel position, only that the handler determines the position. It needs to be consistent in terms of accuracy and precision in the location you have chosen for your dog.

For myself, I want my dog to be about a hand's width from my leg and their shoulder/top of their rib cage to be even with my pant seam (so they will be forged slightly from most standard heel position definitions). I want their head up and looking at my face. I want my dog's tail upright and ear-set forward.

I can create these criteria through the use of training props, such as platforms, and the value of my reward. I can increase the frequency of these criteria through my rate and value of the reinforcement I provide.

I start the process of communicating to my dogs the location of heel position – both on my right and my left – using standing platforms. Even if you have used platforms in the past, you may find some hints and tips here that will help the platforms be more effective for you.

Standing platforms should be long enough for your dog to stand on comfortably and narrow enough that their body can't be angled on the platform.

Why Stand?

Many train heel position as a *sit in heel* rather than a *stand in heel*. I train it the other way around. I teach my dog where heel position is while he is standing. I then add movement, and then once my dog understands my criteria for heeling, I'll add the sit.

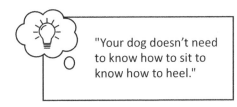

"Your dog doesn't need to know how to sit to know how to heel."

When our dogs are actively heeling, they are standing on all four legs, and not sitting. Often, a lot of focus (and reinforcement) is placed on the set-up in heel, the sit specifically. This can cause the dog to want to sit early, before they are all the way into position. Less focus is placed on that first step into a stand so that the dog and handler can move forward and even less focus is placed on teaching the dog where to be while they are standing and moving.

While heeling, the dog is moving, and not stationary in a sit position. I want my dog to understand where they should be while standing on all four legs. I don't want to become a moving target before my dog has a strong reward history and an understanding of standing in heel position.

Building value in a *stand in heel* position is what is going to allow the dog to seek out and stay in position while moving in any direction. And to figure out exactly where they should sit when we need them to.

Practicing a lot of sits and halts and set-ups can flatten a dog's demeanor for heelwork. We want to create a lot of animation and joy in heeling. So for now we are going to put the sits aside and focus on the stand.

CHAPTER 8:
Standing Platforms

While platforms are not new to dog training or to creating position or location criteria for the dog, Michele Pouliot was the first to introduce them to most freestylers and certainly to me. I don't know if she fully realized then all the different ways that platforms would be utilized. The true value of what she brought to platform training was a protocol we could follow to make full use of its value, in communicating not only precision and accuracy of position but focus, engagement and duration as well.

The standing platform is how I start to train position and is also where I add the criteria of attention and duration, as well as start to add my position cue.

When incorporating the platform into your training it's important to commit to a protocol. Start at the beginning and follow a process. I know many handlers that started using platforms but never fully benefited from them either because they didn't follow through in the process or assumed that once they put their position behaviors on cue, they no longer needed them.

If you have used platforms in the past, when was the last time your dog stood on one? If the answer is "a while ago," or "I can't remember" then you aren't fully benefiting from what standing platforms have to offer.

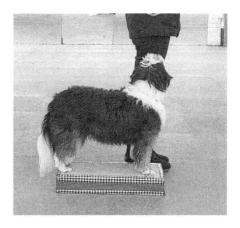

Like other training props, they are a part of my training that I go back to from time to time to refresh my dog's understanding of criteria, maintain a strong reward history, and increase their desire to remain in heel position, whether stationary or moving.

I start to add my "heel" cue when I am working with the platforms. My platforms don't have cues. I don't tell my dog to get up on the platform. A platform is a tool for building behaviors that I *will* put on cue.

If I were to give the platform a cue such as "get on," it can be quite cumbersome to try to transfer that verbal cue to the new verbal cue of "heel." The cue to get on the platform is the presence of the platform. If I don't want my dog on the platform then I don't make it available to them. This makes the transfer to the verbal cue "heel" much cleaner.

It's my responsibility to make sure that where I stand in relation to the platform, and where my dog stands while on the platform, defines my position cue. Only after adding the cue can I start to remove the platform. If I remove the platform before I have attached the cue, there is no information for my dog. The old cue, the platform, is now gone, and the new cue, my position cue is not yet understood.

While I start to add my position cue when working on the standing platform, it isn't until I add that same cue when working with the pivot platform that my dog will start to fully understand the meaning of my heel cue - "No matter where my leg goes, so goes you. Stick to my side and great things happen for you."

How to Make a Standing Platform

Step 1: *Measure your dog's, standing footprint. Add no more than 2-3 inches to the width from the outside measurement of the dog's rear feet. The length needs to be a few inches longer than the space your dog needs to stand comfortably.*

Step 2: *Using the dimensions measured above, cut a piece of foam board insulation to fit your dog's footprint. Foam board insulation is available in hardware or home improvement stores in a variety of sizes. Cut using a long serrated knife or electric carving knife, or for thinner pieces you may be able to score and snap off.*

You want your platform to be about 2-4 inches tall. You may have to stack 2 pieces of foam board to get to that height.

Step 3: *Glue yoga mat pieces to top and bottom of the platform with a glue gun or all-purpose spray adhesive and cover edges and seams with duct tape.*

Step 4: *Optional: Trim edges with decorative duct tape.*

You might consider making the standing platform a dual-purpose platform by making it long enough for your dog to lie down on, so that you could use it for position changes.

Standing Platform Exercises

Guidelines for standing platforms:

1) Your platforms should be large enough for your dog to stand on - too long is generally fine - though you don't want your platform too short or your dog will not feel comfortable standing on it and will appear scrunched with their hind feet under themselves. The width should not be more than 2-3 inches wider than your dog's rear and 1-2 inches on either side.

2) If you are not actively training with your platform, i.e. ready to reward, pick it up and make it unavailable to your dog. That might mean just turning it up on its side or leaning it up on something. For some dogs that won't be enough and you'll need to remove it from view.

3) The cue to get on the platform is the presence of the platform. When training your dog to get on the platform, you won't be giving your dog any other cue. You want to shape your dog to get on the platform, and for him to freely offer it.

Avoid preventing or holding your dog back from getting on the platform if it's available. That would be like saying "come" after tying your dog to a fence. You gave your dog a cue but won't let them complete the behavior. Only when we start to name the positions will your dog start to associate a cue with the platform and its location in relation to you.

Step 1: Shaping Your Dog to Stand on a Platform – Starting the Protocol

1) Start by placing the platform directly in front of you as if it is in "center," or "front" position. Your toes should *not* be right up against the top of the platform. You will want to position yourself so that your dog has enough room for their head to be between you and the top edge of the platform where their front feet will be. Stand straight, with your hands at your side and no food in your hands.

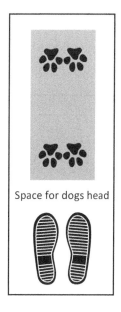

Space for dogs head

2) Mark as soon as your dog notices the platform. Toss your reward directly in front of you, behind the platform a few feet. This provides a fairly straight path back toward you with the platform directly in the dog's path. Try not to toss too far. You don't want your dog becoming engaged with

something else or searching endlessly for the treat. After your dog eats the treat and moves to you (and the platform), mark then toss your treat in the same way. For your first few reps, mark your dog approaching the platform, before your dog reaches the end of it. You can then increase your criteria for your dog to move more fully onto the platform.

3) After a few successful reps of marking your dog for moving toward the platform, withhold your marker to encourage your dog to move further onto the platform. Don't wait for all four feet to be up there before marking. Continue to increase your criteria with successive reps until all four feet are on the platform. Some dogs will continue to move onto the platform after the click or other marker, others will stop in their tracks. Either is fine.

If your dog has less than four feet on the platform, the treat gets tossed behind them (and the platform). Once your dog has four feet on, provide a little *Fast Food* to build value in being on the platform, before tossing one to reset your dog for another rep.

Step 2: Introducing Left and Right Heel Positions

Once your dog is moving onto the platform, we can transition the platform to left or right heel positions. Your platform defines the dog's location in relation to you.

If you are training for freestyle, you will want to work both your left and right sides. This can be done in the same or different sessions. If you are training for obedience, consider training both left and right sides for better symmetry in muscle development and use.

Your positions do not have to be trained to fluency or on cue before working on the other positions (in freestyle there are several). You can work on all of them.

If your dog already finds value, and is "magnetized" to the platform, meaning your dog can't wait to get on and stay on the platform, you can start the exercises in heel

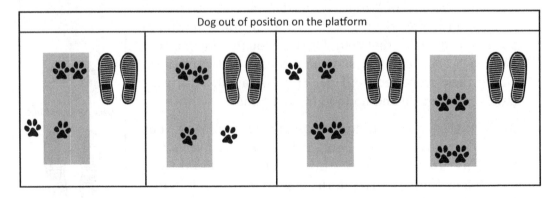
Dog out of position on the platform

position. If not then first focus on shaping your dog to the platform in front of you. Once the value is there and they are "magnetized," you can place the platform to your left and/or right sides in "heel" position.

With each new position that you place the platform, your dog's understanding of the process and learning of positions will improve and each new position will take less time to train than the last.

1) Place the platform on your left or right side

2) Toss a treat behind you and the platform so your dog again has a straight path to the platform, just as they did when the platform was in front of you.

Remain looking ahead, even though you tossed behind, especially as your dog moves back toward the platform after eating the treat. Looking behind you as your dog moves to the platform will create a picture you don't want your dog to see - that of your body angled. You may want to use a mirror or if using a phone or tablet to video, flip the camera and use a setting that allows you to view what you are videoing.

3) Mark as your dog moves toward the platform. Be conservative to start, shaping your dog to the platform to ensure confidence with the new position.

4) If your dog brings all four feet onto the platform, provide some *Fast Food* with your hand closest to the dog. Reaching across your body to deliver a reward can result in either you or the dog becoming out of alignment. The dog may try to reach across, turning their head too far in, in anticipation of reward, and causing their rear to swing out. And while this may not be noticeable as they work to stay on the platform, it becomes obvious once the platform is no longer there to guide them.

If your dog comes onto the platform with less than four feet, reward using a reset toss behind the platform.

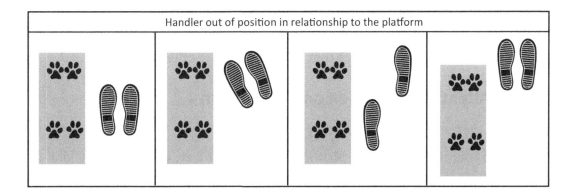

Handler out of position in relationship to the platform

There is a saying among platform users "if the dog is on the platform, he's correct." Meaning that the platform defines the space that is our criteria and if the dog is on it, they should be rewarded. The platform puts the dog where we want them to be so that we can provide a high rate of reward. But while the dog may be correct, the handler could be incorrect.

You'll want to make sure that where you are standing in relation to the platform when your dog is on it, is where you want your dog to be once the platform is removed. If you are not straight and in line with the platform, then your dog is not in heel position, even though they may be on the platform. Just as if your platform is too wide for your dog, they will be able to be out of position, even though the platform is "in position."

If your platform is the perfect length and fits your dog's footprint exactly then you will stand where you want your dog to be in relation to your leg. This is your heel position. Again, be sure to look to the definition of heel position in your sport of choice.

If your dog tends to lag, you will want to stand in correct position in relation to your dog with their back feet at the back of the platform. If they tend to forge, stand in a correct position in relation to the dog so that the dog's front feet are at the front of the platform.

Step 3: Adding Attention and Duration as Criteria

In adding any new criteria, I first ask myself "is the current criteria predictable?" Would I bet something of value that my dog will do it again? If my dog has just met the criteria four or five times in a row, then I have a pretty safe bet.

My prediction though may change depending on the environment or other factors affecting the dog such as other dogs nearby or other attractions in the environment. So even if your dog has been predictable in the past or in other environments, err on the side of caution and test with a couple of successful reps before increasing criteria in new environments or adding difficulty.

Once you can predict within a session that your dog will get onto the platform confidently with all four feet, it is time to increase your criteria.

Adding Attention to Position on the Platform

The next criterion I add is attention or eye contact.

As soon as your dog gets on the platform with all four feet, wait until they look up in anticipation of a treat, and then mark. Again, if four feet are on, provide a little *Fast Food* to continue to build value in being on the platform before tossing a treat to reset.

Criteria shifts are one of the most difficult concepts for trainers to apply. That piece of training where we need to push the limits to get to the next level, the next little bit of criteria that takes us closer to the end behavior, the final product.

When and how to increase criteria is a process that many trainers struggle with. It's often described as a linear or stair-step process, yet when you are in the throes of it, it feels anything but linear! Raising criteria can be messy! Even for the best of trainers. There is often a little bit of guessing that goes on before sliding into a place where you feel you made the right choice. That doesn't mean you don't want to strive for a clean, linear process.

Once I start to see confidence and predictability in a specific criterion, that tells me my dog understands that criterion or piece of the behavior. It's time to raise my criteria.

If I am seeing a lack of consistency or confidence, then my dog doesn't fully understand that criterion or piece of the behavior. It's time to lower my criteria.

Progress doesn't happen without going outside of our comfort zone just a little, just enough to progress to the next set of successes that will take us closer to our goals. Nor does it happen if we continue to ask our dog for something he doesn't fully understand.

Criteria shifts are in effect, asking your dog what they understand.

Clean Loops

The term "loopy training" is one that Alexandra Kurland uses to describe the rhythm that occurs when a dog is confident in a behavior or criterion that earns reinforcement. A "loop" is created through the predictability of reinforcement, which includes the cue, (prompt or antecedent arrangement) for the behavior to occur, then the marker, followed by reinforcement. When the "loop" is rhythmic and predictable, it can indicate understanding and confidence.

It's this understanding and confidence that gives us an indication that the dog is ready for an increase in criteria. Stay too long in the loop and it can be hard for the dog to move up to the next criterion. Not staying long enough though won't create the predictability and confidence we need the dog to have to build strength in that piece of the behavior.

In clean loops, there are no extraneous behaviors, nothing that doesn't benefit the criteria. If your loop is "loose" and other behaviors or criteria are creeping in, you want to try to close the loop a bit. These extraneous behaviors can find their way into your goal behavior, creating latency or unwanted chains. Be observant of the loop and what it includes.

If your dog is getting up on the platform predictably, but not offering to look up at you, you can make a little sound, or say their name to encourage them to look up and then mark. Your dog shouldn't need this kind of prompt more than a couple of times before they start to anticipate and look up at you when they get on to the platform.

Adding Duration

When your dog is predictably getting on the platform with four feet and looking up at you, you can add a little duration. By adding duration to attention, you are also adding duration to the position. Both criteria must be met to earn the reward. When marking for duration, your marker comes at the end of the duration criteria.

When adding duration, we are simply adding time as part of our criteria. However, we need the criterion to be measurable. A "little more" is vague at best and ambiguous at worst. Having clear criteria when adding duration is what defines success. Defining duration as 2 seconds, or 3 seconds, or 4 seconds adds clarity for both the dog and the handler. For many of us, it can be difficult to keep track of time. Especially when we are trying to determine the number of seconds as our criterion.

It's not uncommon when building duration for us to get "stuck" at the same length of time i.e. we always have our dog stay for X number of seconds, or we always take X number of steps. To be sure that I am increasing my duration, I count. Sometimes to myself, but often out loud. Start with 1 second, mark and reward. Build to 2 seconds, mark and reward, 3 seconds, etc.

If I count out loud, I like to make my voice sound like praise. The dog doesn't know that what I'm saying are numbers. What they hear is the tone I use when I praise them. At the very least, smile! For a dog that is trained that if they don't receive information in the form of a marker or reward they should try again or try something else, building duration can be challenging for the handler. Giving some feedback can be helpful for some dogs.

If you struggle with building duration, counting (whether out loud or in your head) gives you a clear measurement on which to build.

In general, while on the platform, you will want to build to about 4-5 seconds of head up with eye contact or looking at a focal point. Since I am continually reinforcing attention and focus in my training, it is continually being offered. Attention, or eye contact as a behavior (including added difficulty such as duration and distractions) should be trained and reinforced using a variety of exercises outside of platform training. If you've been rewarding for eye contact, this part will go relatively quickly.

Step 4: Adding Angles of Entry

When your dog is coming up onto the platform predictably, with eye contact and a few seconds of duration you can start to add a new criterion: Getting onto the platform from different angles.

For many dogs, adding this bit of challenge and more physicality increases the enjoyment in this often stationary work.

1) Toss the treat behind you, but at a slight angle to the left or right of where you have been tossing. Mark, reward, and repeat with the same angle.

2) If your dog is successful at coming fully onto the platform for a few reps, sharpen your angle, tossing at a 90-degree angle to the side of the platform.

3) When they are successful there, toss so the angle is even more difficult, in front of you and the platform.

When planning your reset tosses, using the image of a funnel or clock face can help to ensure you are varying the dog's angles of entry.

Initially mark just this new criterion: All four feet on the platform from varying angles of entry. Make this a fast-paced game initially, before adding back in the criterion of looking up at your face.

Overview on Shaping

Shaping is a method of training used to build a skill or behavior incrementally, using successive approximations. The skill or behavior being trained is broken down into smaller components which are each reinforced. These components build on each other, terminating in the final goal behavior. This creates a high rate of reward during the training process and a stronger understanding of criteria.

For example, to shape a dog to get in their crate, you would start by rewarding the dog for looking toward the crate. Once the dog is looking toward the crate predictably, you would then shift your criteria and mark and reward for moving toward the crate, and finally into the crate. You would increase your criteria for reward incrementally, each criterion taking several reps to build value and reward history before increasing. Behaviors may be broken down into many more steps than indicated here, depending on the complexity of the skill and the confidence and understanding the dog is showing.

Step 5: Naming the Position

When your dog is predictably meeting the criteria of getting all four feet on the platform from various angles and is able to hold the position with attention and duration for a few seconds you are ready to start the process of naming your positions. Note you are not naming the platform, but the position the platform is in, in relation to you.

After tossing the treat to reset your dog, watch for a "commitment point." That is the point at which you are 80% certain the dog is going to put all four feet onto the platform. Give your verbal cue for that position ("heel" or "right" or whatever your cue will be for that position). Mark, toss your reward as a reset, repeat. It is this repetition that will help to connect the cue to the action of moving to the position, with the platform as a placeholder. On some reps, give a little *Fast Food* to build value in the position following the cue.

At this point, your dog isn't getting on the platform because you gave the cue. We are only associating the cue with the dog moving into that position, something they are doing because of the reward history, not the cue itself. So don't think for a minute that the dog understands the cue after a few reps or even after a few sessions. There are several exercises we'll do to help the dog understand the meaning of position cues. This is just the start.

Even if you have strong positions and position cues it will benefit you to run through the platform steps anyway. If you don't have strong positions or feel they could be stronger, then you want to go through all the steps. Using a platform is one of the clearest ways to introduce your dog to the criteria and meaning you want your position cues to have.

Adding the Cue

Adding a cue to a behavior is a process, and a fluid one at that! There are several considerations that play a role in when and how to add the cue.

In determining when to add a cue to a newly trained behavior, or behavior in training, I first ask myself these questions:

🐾 Are the primary and essential components of the behavior present and predictable?

🐾 Is my dog showing confidence in the execution?

If I can answer yes to these questions then I will insert my cue just before the behavior occurs, starting the process of adding the cue, and associating the cue with the behavior.

The answer to these questions may change depending on the behavior, the environment, or other conditions. If I am uncertain as to whether my dog will execute the behavior, I may decide not to provide the cue and will rely on other antecedents to elicit the behavior.

We use cues as a means to elicit a response from our dogs. Our dogs use cues to provide a path to reward. To teach the dog the meaning and value of a cue, we need it to predict both the behavior and the resultant reward.

There is always an antecedent, precursor, or trigger to any behavior. In training new behaviors, often those are the conditions set forth in our sessions – available reinforcement, the presence of a prop, or holding the clicker. These are all conditions that tell our dogs to provide behavior and that their action can lead to reward.

Our job is to be able to predict the occurrence of the behavior and insert our new cue into the sequence.

For example: In adding the new cue "heel" to the position to our left, the standing platform is our known cue. We can predict that our dog will move to and come into the correct position, on the platform. So we can insert our verbal cue "heel" just before they do. Reward results and our dog begins to associate the new cue with the behavior and resulting reward.

On a pivot platform, if we can predict our dog will move into us when we take a step away, then we can insert the cue just before we take the step. The platform and the step away is the known cue, and our verbal "heel" is our new cue.

New Cue Followed by Known Cue

The protocol for teaching a dog the meaning of a new cue is "new cue followed by known cue." Why is the order important? In adding a cue to a behavior we want to create an anticipatory relationship between the known or old cue and the new cue. Our dog will learn the pattern that the known cue will follow the new cue. They can anticipate and begin to provide the behavior on the new cue, not waiting for the known cue. This allows a speedier path to reward, which is the goal of most dogs (and handlers!).

Removing the standing platform

Once your dog is showing a strong understanding of getting up on the standing platform with all four feet, can do so at different angles of entry and with a few seconds of eye contact and duration, and you have started to add the cue, you can begin the process (yes, It's a process!) of removing the platform. Removal is done over several sessions.

Using a mirror will really help in removal. Again you want to try to avoid twisting back to look at your dog as they get the tossed treats.

Step 1: Physically removing the platform should be practiced before working the exercise with your dog. If you have a large dog, the act of picking up the platform and maneuvering it out of the way can be difficult. Especially if your platform is a little heavy.

Work in an area that allows you to place the platform within easy reach, but out of the way and not flat on the ground so that it doesn't act as a cue for the dog. When you pick up the platform, it's best to place it on a nearby table, or lean it against a chair or wall.

Step 2: After marking for the correct response of all four feet in position on the platform, toss your treat far enough behind to give you time to lift the platform up and place it within reach but in a position that your dog cannot get onto it.

Do not move from your spot! You want your dog to see the exact same picture when they turn back toward you. Give your heel cue. We are betting on the pattern you have created to help them move towards heel. Towards heel, not into heel.

Mark early - as your dog is moving towards/into heel. You are going to back up a little in shaping the dog's position, so don't get greedy or you are going to end up with a frustrated dog that doesn't know what to do. In other words, don't wait for heel position on the first few reps. Mark the approach to heel position to start and gradually increase your criteria to being fully in position.

Step 3: After 1-2 reps of tossing your treat behind you, put your platform back down. Therefore it needs to be within reach. Again, you don't want your dog to see you move.

When removing the platform we are going to alternate or ping-pong between with the prop and without the prop, easy and hard, in position and toward position. Be prepared to spend a bit of time in this phase.

Step 4: Gradually start to withhold your marker until your dog is coming all the way into position. Each time your dog is successful at coming all the way into position, provide *Fast Food*.

Ping-Pong

Ping-Ponging is a term used to describe a process of alternating between an increased or more difficult task or criterion, with an easier task or criterion. It allows the dog a respite from always having to work harder and harder as we build the dog's skills. It provides a slight relief from pressure, giving the dog a chance to build more confidence before venturing into the next, possibly more difficult repetition. It can teach a dog to persevere as our criteria continues to increase.

Don't make assumptions! Just because your dog is successful a few times doesn't mean you are ready to completely remove the platform. This will take several sessions, and still, you will want to go back to the platform on occasion to build value and "make it easy" to maintain confidence.

Select for Stronger Responses

As you work through the process of ping-ponging the platforms and re-shaping your criteria, and your history of reward for position is strong, start to select for stronger responses. By that I mean withhold your marker if your dog isn't meeting the full criteria.

By withholding your marker we are 1) asking the dog what they understand and 2) encouraging them to think through why you aren't marking and 3) allowing them to correct any errors or lesser criteria.

We are transferring some responsibility for finding the position to our dog.

CHAPTER 9:
Using Training Gates or Barriers

I developed the use of training gates out of necessity in working with Kashi, my Tibetan Terrier who had severe food sensitivities. During the time we were trying to diagnose her, while training she would start to feel ill after eating even just a few pieces of food.

Not wanting to associate training with not feeling well, I looked for a way to clearly communicate precision criteria to her using the least amount of food rewards.

The use of these low barriers allowed us to continue to enjoy our training sessions with fewer food rewards, yet still be able to meet training goals. The training gates gave me an effective and more efficient way to train precision criteria.

What are Training Gates?

Training gates are flexible barriers that can be set up in different configurations depending on what criteria you are wanting to convey to your dog. They are similar to a miniature ex-pen but much shorter, between 10 and 14 inches in height. The dog is aware of them, but they are not as obvious as a solid barrier. For heelwork, they will generally be set up in a straight line, so any straight, low barrier will work.

When I start to convey criteria using a barrier, I set it up similar to where I would place my platform. I want the area my dog will move to, the area defined by the gates or barrier, to be no larger than the area I want them to occupy in heel position.

For the platforms to be effective training tools, we need to do some "pre-training" – that is, shape the dog to get on and stay on with all four feet. We

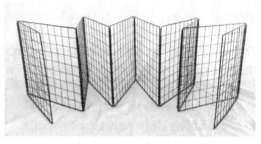

need to build a reward history and value in getting on and staying on the platform. When using training gates or barriers, once we acclimate and ensure that the dog is comfortable working around the barrier, we can start using them right away to convey criteria.

Again, a mirror or a way to see behind you is useful so that you can remain facing forward and that the picture your dog sees from behind or the side isn't one of your hips or shoulders twisting back.

Step 1: Set your gates or barrier up in a straight line. Be sure your barrier is stable and will not fall over. If you are using the training gates, fold the end panels for stability.

Step 2: Lure or encourage your dog next to you, between you and the gates or other barrier. If using the gates you can fold the front panel in to prevent your dog from moving too far forward.

Provide some *Fast Food* to your dog in position to build value.

Step 3: Toss your treat behind you. Toss to the outside of your dog's back hip, so that they turn away from you to get the treat. To give your dog space to make the turn you can step slightly away from them before tossing. If the front is open, they can also move forward and around the gate to get the treat. As your dog returns to the position, mark and provide *Fast Food* to continue to build value in the position before resetting.

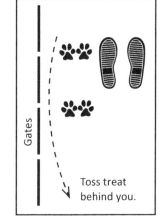

Toss treat behind you.

As mentioned, you can turn one panel in at the front to prevent your dog from moving too far forward. Or to discourage lagging, you can keep the front open and after *Fast Food*, toss the reward forward so your dog moves forward to the treat. Then toss a second treat to reset behind you.

Step 4: Add your attention and duration criteria just as you would for the platforms. Mark after your dog comes into position and looks up at you, or at your pre-determined focal point. Gradually increase the duration, marking at the end of your duration criteria for that rep.

Step 5: As with the platform, add angles of entry to ensure your dog can find the position from any location.

Add your cue when you can predict your dog will meet your criteria by moving into the defined space between you and the gates from various angles, providing attention and a few seconds of duration. Give your heel cue as they move into position following a tossed reward. Mark when all your previous criteria is met.

As you can see, the process is identical to using the platform. Using the gates in conjunction with the platform, alternating sessions, can be highly effective in reinforcing your criteria.

Fading out the gates is done a bit differently than with the platform.

Removing the Gates

When removing the gates, as with the platform, you want to be as inconspicuous as you can. You don't want the dog highly aware of the change.

Step 1: Rather than physically removing the gates, you are going to shift your position to just forward of the gates.

Toss your treat from the previous rep. When your dog returns from getting the tossed treat, they will see the same picture – you facing away on one side and the gate on the other. While your dog was getting the treat, you will have moved to just ahead of the gate so that when your dog is in position, their head and shoulders are out of the gates.

Step 2: As with the platforms you will ping-pong or alternate being a bit in front of the gate and back in the gate. As your dog becomes more aware of the reward history out of the gate, along with the other exercises you will be doing to convey the criteria of heel position, you'll be able to eliminate the gates completely. When making these subtle changes be sure to provide *Fast Food* prior to your reset toss to continue to build value in the position.

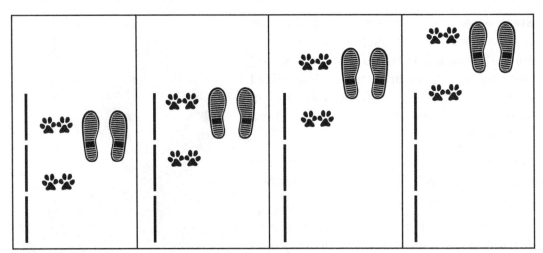

Under the Radar

When removing either the platforms or the training gates for these exercises, you want their removal to be as inconspicuous and discreet as possible. We want the pattern we have created to be maintained, with or without the prop. Continuing to use any single prop or aid for an extended period in all sessions can cause the dog to view the prop as an integral part of the behavior.

By using different props (such as platforms and barriers) to convey the same criteria (heel position in this case) we can more easily separate the prop from the behavior when adding the cue prior to removing the props.

Notes:

CHAPTER 10:
Shaping for Robust Position

One of the most effective ways to build a robust behavior is to shape it. Platforms and gates set up the environment to provide the most obvious path for the dog. This is what I refer to as "structured shaping." We are structuring the environment to make it easier for the dog to provide correct responses and to build a reward history for the position.

However, shaping without the aid of props can greatly enhance your dog's understanding of where heel position is and allow them to really internalize how to get there.

How does shaping relate to joy though? When done effectively, there is a very high rate of reward. If we are clear in our criteria, the dog drives the process and can control that rate. A dog's ability to increase rewards also increases joy! And, it has been argued that giving the dog agency and choice can act as reinforcement.

Yet shaping can be difficult for both dog and handler when it comes to shifting criteria. It can be difficult for handlers to visualize or even articulate the next criteria shift, either up or down. Props such as platforms and gates can help handlers be more clear in their criteria.

Shaping, Confidence and Joy

In shaping to heel, your dog is in control. If you are providing good information through your marker and reinforcement, they can meet criteria, resulting in reward. Being in control of reinforcement, of outcomes, results in confidence.

Confidence is a manner of performance, that presents as behavior - something we can observe. It is charged with enthusiasm and in the ability to handle any resulting outcome. Confidence reflects understanding.

Confidence results in that HER - "Happy Emotional Response." It is not the emotion itself, but rather the feeling that results in the outward behavior, the lift, the head up, the overall appearance of confidence and joy.

Having a visual aid for the handler to identify the criteria helps to create clarity. There are a couple of ways that I use visual aids for the handler that struggles with criteria shifts.

Visualizing Criteria

Using two different colors of mats to define an area can help you to articulate criteria and be better able to see and mark when the criterion occurs. Different color yoga mats work well for this. They are thin enough that they won't act as a platform, yet come in a variety of colors, and are often reversible, making it easy to have 2 contrasting colors to work with.

Cut one color mat to be half again as long as your dog and at least twice as wide. The other color mat will be about the same size as your dog's standing platform, making sure that there are only about two inches outside of your dog's footprint all the way around. Place the smaller mat on top of the larger mat.

Light gray mat extends under black, so criterion of '4 paws on grey' includes the grey under the black.

End goal location for dog — same size as your standing platform.

Different colors create visual aid for the handler to determine criteria shifts — of how many paws in each color.

Step 1: Stand next to the mat that is the size of your standing platform as if you are working on a platform exercise. Toss a treat behind the mat.

When your dog first approaches, your criteria should be low: One foot in either color (size) mat. That is all you are watching for – that first criterion of a single foot on either mat. Mark as soon as you see it and toss your treat behind you to reward and set up for the next repetition.

Step 2: After a few successful reps, you can increase your criteria. Continue to toss the treat behind you for an easy entry for your dog.

For example, you can mark and reward two paws on either color mat.

"There is knowing how to find the position, and there is knowing how to find the position with joy."

Then three paws on either color mat.

Then two paws on the smaller colored mat.

And finally, you will work up to marking all four paws on the smaller colored mat.

When increasing criteria here, your dog drives the process. They will often move ahead, offering the next shift in criteria. Predictability and confidence should still be present before you intentionally raise your criteria.

Step 3: As with the platform you can then change the angle of your treat toss for a more difficult angle of entry. As you raise your criteria in one area (more difficult angle of entry) you will want to lower your criteria in another area (fewer paws in the larger area of either colored mat). You can then continue to increase or make the angle of entry more difficult until your dog can get all four paws on the smaller mat, next to you in heel position.

Keep in mind, that the mats are not props for the dog – the dog may or may not be aware of their relevance. It doesn't really matter though. The mats are a way to define criteria and a visual for you to determine the timing of your marker. This allows you to shape and build the behavior of moving into heel position from anywhere and at any angle, including in front of you.

Inside the Lines

Using a taped area to define your criteria is also an effective way for you to clearly see and mark your criteria. Remember the tape is not for your dog, rather for you to be able to clearly identify the criterion you want to mark.

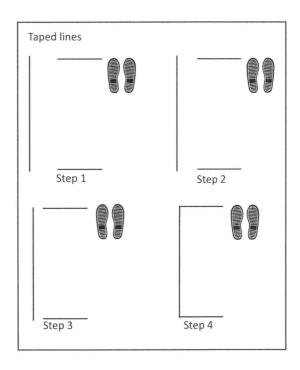

The process is the same as above, however, you will adjust the size of your taped area with each progressive shift of criteria.

There are several ways you can place the tape to help you see if the dog is meeting your criteria, including straight taped lines or angled taped lines or different colors of tape.

Location, Location, Location

Reward Placement or where and how you deliver your reward, can be as important in affecting future behavior as a marker. Our dogs can learn and then anticipate where reward is likely to be presented or delivered, and prepare their bodies for more efficient collection of that reward.

What this means is that we can communicate "correctness" all we want with a marker, but if we are not delivering reinforcement in a way that supports that communication, we could be sabotaging our own training.

To use reward placement to your advantage, consider the actions your dog must take to collect reward.

If the dog is in left heel, and the handler reaches with their right hand into their right pocket and then across their body to deliver the reward, the dog can start to anticipate where that reward is coming from. Instead of moving into a straight heel position, in line with the handler's body, they may start to come in at a slight angle, with their head and muzzle wrapped around the front of the handler and their rear angled out away from the handler, giving them a more advantageous position in which to collect reward.

If on the other hand, the handler rewards with their left hand, slightly to the outside of the dog's head and muzzle, the dog can anticipate that and work to bring their rear closer to the handler in an effort to collect reward more quickly and easily. This anticipation of where reward will be delivered will affect how the dog moves into and remains in heel position. So consider carefully how and where you deliver your reinforcement.

Notes:

CHAPTER 11:
Pivot Platforms

There are a few concepts in dog training that have really impacted the way I communicate with my dogs. Certainly, marker training was a game changer. Props are a close second. I was first introduced to pivot platforms in 2004 by Norwegian trainer Mortven Egtvedt at a dog training conference. The video he shared of his 4-month-old Flat-coated Retriever swinging into heel position convinced me of the ease in which dogs can be taught technical skills. It forever changed how I viewed props in training.

Standing platforms are a great tool for teaching the criteria for stationary positions, a must for dogs to understand. The addition of the pivot platform allows us to add movement, a new criterion, and solidify position cues.

Moving while remaining in position (including laterally and backward), requires the dog to have what we often call "rear-end awareness." While I think that dogs are actually pretty aware of their rear-ends, (ask any dog that has ever sniffed or been sniffed!) they may not always be practiced at using their rear-end in deliberate, thoughtful, and isolated movement.

The pivot platforms are used to teach the dog to isolate their rear-end movement, and to add movement to the position. Along with the standing platforms, the pivot platforms help to create more value in not only staying next to you but in getting there too! This is also where we start to solidify the meaning of our heel cue.

You'll be using the same cue for pivoting as you do for your heeling. We want the dog to do the same behavior here as in heeling – get to position and stay in position, and use their rear-end to do so – no matter where the position goes. If we don't associate our heel cue with pivoting, it will be harder for the dog to figure out that rear-end work is part of heeling. This is why a dog that does a lot of pivot work might still crab or be wide in the rear during heeling. The pivots weren't associated with heeling through the "heel" cue.

The end goal behaviors for the below exercises are moving into left heel (and right heel if you are a freestyler or want to create symmetry in your dog's physicality), strengthening verbal cues for left (and/or right) heel position, pivoting in left (and/or right) heel, and strengthening inside turns.

Step 1: Shaping Your Dog to Stand on the Platform

To shape your dog to the pivot platform, follow the same steps as for the standing platform.

Your pivot platform should be large enough for your dog's front feet, but not so large that there is room for a lot of movement from the front feet without falling off.

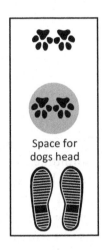
Space for dogs head

> ### Where to Find a Pivot Platform:
>
> *Size Matters! Pivot platforms, like standing platforms are custom to your dog. They should be just large enough for your dog's front feet to fit on. Too large and your dog can start to "dance" or even try to sit on it. Too small and your dog will be worried about falling off.*
>
> *Livestock bowls which can be found at feed stores, can work well as pivot platforms when turned upside down. They are made of rubber and won't slide on the floor and provide your dog with good grip. If you have a large or heavy breed, the livestock bowl may not be firm enough to hold your dog's weight. You can add a block of wood or Styrofoam for support inside the overturned bowl or place two bowls inside of each other.*
>
> *You can also use an upside down dog food dish. Many have a rubber bottom. You may have to use a rubber mat underneath to prevent it from sliding.*
>
> *Or you can make your own using foam board insulation and yoga mat as for the standing platforms or a few stacked foam puzzle mats, taped together with duct tape. Though for larger or more active dogs, a heavier weight platform or sticky mat to prevent sliding may be necessary.*

1) Stand with your toes pointing in toward the platform but not up against the platform. Remember to leave enough room for your dog's head. Your distance from the pivot platform should be about the same as from the standing platform.

2) Mark and reward when your dog has both front feet on the platform. Be sure to include *Fast Food* in this first stage of building value in the platform.

When tossing the treat for a reset, work hard to have your tosses line up directly across from you as we want the dog to come into you in a center/front position.

If the treat toss bounces or you make a bad throw, then you will move to a position directly across from your dog's line of travel, before they move back toward the platform, to ensure that on this first step of the exercise, they come up onto the platform in center/front.

3) Once your dog shows you there is value in the platform and they want to get on, provide some *Fast Food* to them in this center/front position. Do not use a cue for this position at this time. We are only using the high rate of reward in front of you to prepare for the next step. The purpose here is not to teach a front position.

It's not necessary to build duration in this standing/centered position. We just want to ensure the dog understands the need to get on and stay on the platform as you reward. Most of your duration with attention work will happen on your standing platform. The duration will carry over.

Step 2: Creating Rear-end Shifts

After a session of building value through *Fast Food* in the center position, test that value. With your dog centered in front of you on the pivot platform:

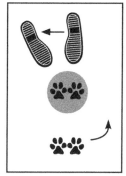

1) Choose the side position that you want to work on (left or right heel). Take a single step around the platform, toes in, in the opposite direction from the side you want your dog to move toward. If you want to work on left heel, step to your right. If you want to work on right heel, step to your left.

If the value for staying in front of you was built in Step 1, your dog will want to remain there. When you move, they will work to stay on the platform and in front of you. This causes the dog to shift their rear in order to remain facing you. Again, we are not teaching a center or front position here. We are only using the value you have built there to create the rear-end shift.

2) When your dog shifts their rear-end to stay in front of you, mark and reward with *Fast Food*. If they do not shift to stay straight in front of you, you can step back in front of your dog to build a little more value through *Fast Food* then try to step again.

3) Continue to step, 1 step at a time in the same direction. Mark and reward any rear-end shift or hind-end movement in the direction of the side you are working. Don't be greedy at first! Mark any movement, however slight, in that direction when you move.

Step 3: Encouraging Independent and Deliberate Movement

1) After a few repetitions of your dog shifting their rear to stay in front of you, change the location of the reward. Instead of rewarding directly in front of you, place the treat so your dog must turn their head slightly in the direction of your step to get the treat.

If you are working toward left heel, use your right hand to feed and if you are working toward right heel use your left hand to feed. In other words, don't reach over your dog's head. Placing your reward in this way will encourage greater degrees of rear-end movement in the direction you want, in future repetitions. It is not meant to lure the dog into a greater degree of movement in the current repetition.

No longer will you step back in front of them. Your dog will likely start to over-shoot your front in anticipation of reward placement. This is good!

2) After several successful repetitions of marking and rewarding in this now over-rotated center position, your dog will start to understand that standing straight in front of you is no longer the criterion to earn the reward, shifting the rear is, and they will start to offer more deliberate movement toward your side.

3) Once your dog is approximately 45 degrees off-center, they will not be able to shift any closer to your side without hitting you or taking their feet off the platform. We want the dog's feet to stay on the platform.

At this point, use your hand closest to your dog to provide a few treats as you turn to move next to your dog. Your toes are no longer pointing toward the pivot platform. You are both now facing the same direction.

> ### *A note about props:*
>
> *Props are great tools that allow us to convey criteria quickly and easily with few errors. Removal of the props doesn't mean that you will never use them again. Their value is not just in teaching criteria, but also in maintaining that criteria. They are also a great way to bring back a bit of fun and joy in your position work! Dogs really seem to enjoy working with props and will often seek them out if they happen to be laying around! If your dog has lost a bit of accuracy or spark in finding position, adding your props back into your training will help provide increased precision, reinforcement and motivation.*

You have placed yourself so your dog is now in perfect heel position. Provide *Fast Food*, giving several treats in a row. This is important for building value here.

Be careful that you aren't so close to your dog that they want to pull away from you or that you are pushing into them. The distance between you and your dog should be the same as if they were on a standing platform.

Step 4: Building Value and Duration in Position

With your dog in the desired position (left or right heel) and their front feet on the pivot platform, with your hand closest to your dog, give several treats in a row to build value in staying in position. Feed with your dog's head straight and level or very slightly out away from you.

1) After your dog finishes the last treat, take one step, starting with your foot closest to your dog, around the platform, and keeping the side of your foot to the platform. Your steps should start out as 90-degree steps so that you are stepping a quarter turn around the pivot platform. Keep your hand at your side or at your hip or belly, and not hover over the bait bag or appear as if food is about to be delivered.

Leading with your closest foot creates a little pressure for your dog to shift back from. Try to avoid doing a shuffle step. Use one foot, take your normal step and then bring your other foot forward to meet it. Stepping in this way also allows the momentum of your dog's rear to bring him further in, and closer to you.

2) When your dog makes any movement in your direction, however small, mark and reward. They will likely stop slightly away from you when you mark. Before feeding, move to your dog to create a perfect heel position. Provide *Fast Food* and praise to build value in this position.

3) Repeat steps 2 and 3 until your dog is working to stay in position next to you when you take the step.

4) Add duration as you did with the standing platforms. Use your voice to give the information to your dog that they are correct, even though you haven't marked yet. Mark and reward

> ### Troubleshooting Platform Avoidance
>
> *Most dogs that have an understanding of getting on the standing platform will take quickly to putting their front feet on the smaller size platform. Some dogs do seem to have difficulty even then. If you have not been successful with either shaping or luring your dog onto the platform by the second or third session, try placing a towel or small covering over the platform. Often the dog will then hop right up.*

at the end of the desired duration. Remember to lower your duration if your dog is having difficulty with maintaining position. Ping-pong duration once you have built up to 3-4 seconds. We want to add a little duration here so the dog doesn't start to think that the pivot platform is a cue to start fishtailing their rear around. Stillness when in heel position is desirable.

5) You want your dog to both move with you but also move to you. Once your dog is confident in moving with you, provide your reward and as you are feeding, take a step away. When your dog is finished eating, they should immediately shift into position next to you. Mark, reward, repeat.

Step 5: Naming the Position - Adding the Cue

Adding your heel cue allows your dog to associate the action of tucking their rear and staying in position with the action of heeling. Teaching the dog to pivot is only of value if they know to use their rear-end while heeling. So use your heel position cue for pivots.

Be sure there is predictability in the behavior, and confidence in the dog's demeanor, before naming or adding the verbal cue. If you would bet something of value that the behavior is about to happen, then insert the verbal cue just before the behavior occurs. NOTE: The verbal cue must be given before you move! Give the *new cue* (verbal) *followed by the known cue* (taking a step).

1) With your dog in position, provide several treats in a row.

2) Give your verbal heel cue, then (not at the same time, but following your verbal cue) take one step, around the platform just as in Step 4. Mark and reward.

If your dog did not move with you, staying in position, go back to Step 4. Do not move to the next step until you have strong consistency and predictability in the previous step.

Add a Challenge

1) Toss your treat a few feet away

2) As your dog moves to you, give your heel cue

3) As your dog reaches the platform, take a step around the platform so they need to work a bit harder to swing into position. Mark and reward, repeat.

Step 6: Removing the Pivot Platform

Once your dog is showing value in the position, both offering to move into you and responding to the cue, you can start the process of removing the platform. Be sure that your dog is confident and there is no latency, or time delay, after you give your cue and take your step.

Removing the pivot platform adds difficulty to the task for the dog. What kept the dog's front feet in position and their rear-end working - the platform - will no longer be there to aid them. Your verbal cue is now what will tell them to shift and remain next to you even though the platform is no longer present.

When we add more difficulty to a task or add more difficult criteria to a behavior, we want to raise our rate of reward and lower criteria in another area of the behavior, before building all criteria back up again. So in this next step, we are going to lower the criterion of the exact position and raise the rate of reward (mark and reward more frequently) for rear-end shifts.

With your dog next to you in position and front feet on the platform, reward several times in position. Give your verbal cue and then take your step around the platform as in Step 4. Repeat a couple of times to ensure you have all the criteria you want when you give the cue.

There are two options I use to physically remove the pivot platform.

Option 1: You can remove the platform by picking it up during a reset toss.

1) Toss your treat a little forward and to the side of the platform. As your dog is moving toward the treat, reach down and pick up your platform. Place it under your opposite arm.

2) Give your verbal cue and mark as your dog is starting to shift into position. Don't wait until they come all the way into position. Mark early, as they move into position, rather than late.

Your dog will likely end up out of position when starting the process of removal and marking early. As you are starting to feed, move to your dog, facing the same direction to create an accurate heel position and reward your dog there.

3) Ping-pong the pivot platform just as we did with the standing platform. This allows your dog to be in the correct position most of the time while transitioning off the platform. We want to use the pattern of correctness we created with the platform, to create that same pattern in the absence of the platform.

Once you have removed the platform in one session, that does not mean you are done! You will need to start the next session with the platform, then move through the process of removal again, which should go much more quickly.

If you are successful at this point, don't expect your dog to remember from session to session the last point of success, i.e. just because you were able to get a few nice pivots on the flat, doesn't mean you will start on the flat on your next session. When you first start a session without the platform, remember to mark for much lower criteria and then build from there. At each session, start a couple steps back in the process for at least a few sessions so you are confident your dog fully understands each step in the process. Don't rush this. Don't expect your dog to do well at the next step if they haven't mastered the previous one.

Option 2: You can also remove the platform from under the dog. This is best suited to smaller dogs.

1) With the hand closest to your dog, hold food at your dog's nose, even allowing them to nibble, to keep them close. Use your far hand to bend down and remove the platform from under your dog.

Depending on the size and weight of your dog, this could take a few seconds, so have plenty of food in your hand to keep your dog busy. If you have a very large or heavy dog you can use the food to move them off slightly, so you can get the platform out from under your dog.

2) Work hard to remain in place, or move only minimally. Place the pivot platform on a nearby table or hold it under your arm. As with the standing platform, you want to be as inconspicuous as possible when removing the platform. You don't want the picture to change. You will not be doing any tossing of treats when you remove the platform for this exercise.

When the dog's feet come off the platform it will take them somewhat out of position. Change *your* position so your dog is now back in heel position and provide a bit of *Fast Food*.

3) Stop feeding and when your dog looks up, give your verbal cue and take a step exactly as if the platform were there. Mark and reward any small movement toward you! Do not expect your dog to move fully into you.

Be sure to mark as your dog is moving and not after your dog has stopped. We are shaping your criteria back up to what it was with the pivot platform in place

Again, as you are feeding, move so that you are next to your dog and they are back in an accurate heel position. You are creating this accuracy in position by moving next to your dog. Provide *Fast Food*.

4) Then repeat: Give the verbal cue, then step as if the bowl is there, mark and reward any movement into you, move so that you are back in perfect heel position, and provide *Fast Food*. After just 1 or 2 reps, toss your treat and place the platform back in position. Ping pong your reps, with and without the platform.

Supplemental methods:

If your dog is struggling with shifting their rear, Hannah Branigan has a nice way of getting a dog started and confident in the action. Below is a brief description. Hannah explains this in detail in her book *Awesome Obedience*.

With your dog on the pivot platform, for your dog to shift to the left, their rear moving counter-clockwise, use your left hand over the dog's head. Place your left foot forward so that your left hip is toward the platform. If you are wanting to work your right side heel position, then your right hand and foot are forward.

Hold a handful of treats over the pivot platform above your dog's head, with knuckles down so that if you open your hand, your palm is facing up. As your dog looks up at your closed hand holding the food, they will shift their rear for a better view. Mark then turn your hand to feed. Your dog's head will remain over the platform, though slightly turned out. Continue until your dog is confidently performing in 360 degrees with his rear around the pivot platform. Then step in and reward in position.

Square Pivots

Using the training gates is another option for working on pivots. Having the panels in the configuration of a square will help to clearly define the criteria.

Step 1: Place your gates in a square pen, with you in the center facing one of the panels and your dog in heel position. Provide some *Fast Food* to build value in the position.

Step 2: Give your verbal heel cue. Then, leading with your foot closest to your dog, take the same 90-degree step you would as if you were stepping around a pivot platform. Mark and reward as your dog shifts with you to remain in position. You should now be facing the next panel.

Step 3: Continue to give your verbal heel cue, followed by single 90-degree steps, marking and rewarding your dog for moving with you a single step, in position.

Step 4: As your dog's understanding and confidence grows, you can start to fold back or eliminate 1-2 sides of the square so that your dog is getting less aid from the gates before eliminating them completely.

Once your dog has some experience pivoting into you while on the pivot platform, this exercise can help solidify your dog's understanding when off the platform. I prefer to have the dog have some reward history for choosing to shift their rear into you before going into the square gates. For many dogs it can help them better understand the criteria.

Square pivots can also help to mitigate over-rotating by alternating between a back pivot (left turn if the dog is on your left and right turn if your dog is on your right) and a forward pivot (right turn if your dog is on your left, and left turn if your dog is on your right). The guidance that the gates provide prevent the dog from swinging wide on outside pivots or turns.

Props, Props and more Props!

You may be wondering if all these props are really necessary? If you are using a standing platform, do you really need the training gates? And if you are using the training gates for pivots, do you really need a pivot platform? Maybe!

Props convey criteria, but we don't always know which prop will make the most sense to the dog. By providing multiple ways to convey criteria, not only are we assured that the dog will get the message but getting that same message in multiple ways can help solidify knowledge and understanding.

If props aren't removed at an appropriate point in the training process, the prop can become an integral part of the behavior, making removal difficult. By using multiple props to convey the same criteria, and those criteria are attached to the same cue, the process of removing the props can go much more smoothly and quickly. The dog doesn't associate any single prop with the behavior, rather the behavior and the attached cue become foremost in importance and not the prop.

Notes:

CHAPTER 12:

Adding More Joy
to Your Platform Exercises

The platform exercises allow us to define and communicate the more technical components of heelwork. They allow the dog to better understand the concept of accuracy and build value in stillness in position. They also allow us to connect other criteria, such as focus and attention toward the handler.

While dogs do tend to enjoy working with platforms or props due to the high rate of reward (and the reset tosses are all about the fun game of chasing food!) when compared to some of the other more active games you may feel your dog could benefit from integrating more movement or some of the other construct games.

Below are a few ways you can do just that!

Jump for Joy with Standing Platforms

This is not only a great way to add the fun of the hand touch to your platform work, but it also allows you to refine your hand target position. Your dog is also learning to control their body and work to maintain a position in relation to you.

How to Play the Game:

Step 1: Start with a few reps of your dog moving to the standing platform following a tossed treat. Then practice a few hand touches or *Jump to Food* on the platform with your dog stationary. It may take a few reps for your dog to feel comfortable coming off their front feet while on the platform - keep your hand low enough so that they only need to come up a few inches.

Step 2: After a reset toss, give your heel cue for your dog to come to position on the platform. When your dog returns to the platform, present your hand for *Jump to Hand*, and follow up with *Jump to Food*. Your dog will learn to maintain an accurate position even while shifting their weight to their rear and lifting their front feet a little.

Step 3: You can add your eye contact and duration criteria before presenting your hand as a secondary reinforcer followed by the jump for food and tossed treat.

Pivot If You Cone!

This game can be played either with your pivot platform or while pivoting on the flat. It adds the familiar (and fun!) construct game of *Out and Around* the cone to the pivot exercises.

How to Play the Game:

Step 1: Start with your cone in front of you, about 6-10 feet away, and your dog on the pivot platform, next to you in heel position. Send your dog to go *Out and Around* the cone. As they round the cone, give your heel cue. Mark and reward when your dog comes into heel position.

Step 2: From here you can either send your dog to the cone again, or do a pivot with your dog until you are back again facing the cone, before sending for another rep.

Step 3: Add some challenge! Pivot to a point where the cone is not directly in front of you but

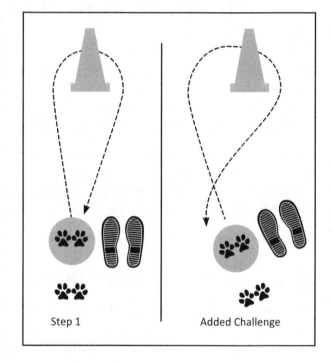

Step 1   Added Challenge

off to the side. Send your dog and give your heel cue. Can they still come back to you and find the position even if you move again?

Be sure to provide *Fast Food* when they do! Finding that position again is all about the value you've put into it.

Heel If You Cone!

This is similar to *Pivot If You Cone*! We'll be adding the standing platform.

How to Play the Game:

Step 1: Place your cone in the area ahead of you and the standing platform, about 6-10 feet away. Send your dog to go *Out and Around* the cone.

Give your heel cue and when your dog returns to the standing platform in position, reward with *Fast Food* before sending around the cone for another rep.

Step 2: Add a challenge! There are several variations of this game that include just your left side heel or both your left and right side heel in the same exercise, providing your dog with some experience with cue discrimination.

In these variations, you can change your position, either in relation to your dog, or in relation to the platform. By changing your position in relation to the dog, ie turning so that your back is now to the dog as they round the cone, or changing your position in relation to the platform (so the platform is now on your other side), you can give your dog either their right side cue or left side cue depending on what side of the platform you move to.

You'll need to be quick! You want to get to the different orientation before your dog rounds the cone so that you have time to give your cue before they get onto the platform.

Front Cross Pivots - Cue discrimination on the pivot platform

In this game, you will be working pivots on both the left and right sides, with a single pivot platform. The catch is that your dog's feet will never leave the pivot platform, even when changing sides!

How to Play the Game:

Step 1: Start with your dog's front feet on the pivot platform, standing next to you in either left or right side heel position.

Step 2: Give your cue for the position on the opposite side and start to turn 180 degrees toward and into your dog (and the pivot platform) so that you will be facing the other direction on the *same side of the pivot platform*. The side that you had cued your dog to move to is now available to them. Mark and provide *Fast Food*. Repeat to the other side!

Your dog may need some prompting initially. Using the hand closest to your dog with a hand cue or lure, encourage your dog to turn into you, as you turn into them, opening up the other side to them.

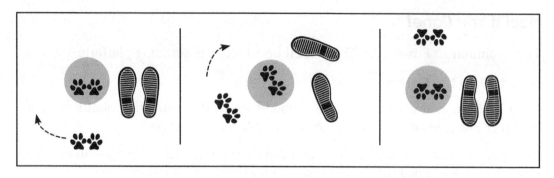

Step 3: Add a challenge! After a few reps of cueing and moving side to side, instead of cueing to the other side, continue your steps around the platform, having your dog pivot to stay with you. This will help your dog to start to focus more on your cues rather than assume they will be automatically moving to the other side.

Notes:

_____

_____

_____

_____

_____

_____

_____

_____

_____

_____

_____

_____

_____

_____

_____

_____

_____

_____

_____

PART IV

More Games! More Joy!

"There is no such thing as too much happiness"
— Drew Carey

CHAPTER 13:

Get Moving!

While the games and exercises all have value on their own, they are most beneficial when worked together. Combining the games will help give you and your dog the most complete picture of joyful heeling!

Heel With Me! Play With Me!

For this game, we are going to alternate and integrate a game of tug or personal play into short bits of heeling.

This game can be played on or off cue – meaning you can use your heel cue if it has meaning to your dog, or you can work this with offered criteria.

Ideally, your dog will release their toy readily when asked. If not you can use a bit of bowling to help them release the toy when transitioning from play to heeling. You will want to work on relinquishing toys outside of these sessions. This should be an active game that transitions from play to heel and back to play quickly and seamlessly.

How to Play the Game:

Step 1: Engage your dog in play! It can be personal play, or you can use a tug or toy. Make sure it is a style of play or activity your dog enjoys.

Step 2: After a few seconds, mid-session, and without the formality of the set-up, start to move forward. As your dog falls into position alongside you, mark and start to play again! If your dog does not continue to engage in an effort to get alongside you, go back to your *Food Bowling* or *Jump for Joy games*.

Step 3: You can gradually extend and ping-pong the amount of heeling that meets your criteria before marking and going back to play!

Just Do It!

This is an extension of the *Heel With Me! Play With Me!* game. Here we are shifting to either low-key personal play or more casual interaction. We want our dogs looking for the opportunity to heel with us, which causes us to start another game. This isn't a total replacement for *Heel With Me! Play With Me!* but an adjunct to it, so that your dog learns to play the game with or without a toy or other external motivators present.

Just as in *Heel With Me! Play With Me!* when playing the game *Just Do It!* there are no set-ups, no starting in heel postion, no having the dog sit, no getting the dog into any particular position. Instead, you can start this with a bit of personal play or other interaction such as engaging your dog in conversation.

If your dog struggles with the personal play part, try a game of chase, or move quickly in any direction away from your dog. Movement creates interest. When your dog comes in close, you can turn and start to move forward, providing the opportunity for your dog to move with you and seek out heel position.

Remember that in competition, there is only you in the ring so you want to start to integrate some personal interaction into the start of the games. You will still reinforce but we want the dog to be looking for opportunities to heel - to push you into a game of *Jump for Joy* or *Food Bowling*. If your dog still struggles with engaging with you when you don't have food or toys, you can jump-start with a bit of *Food Bowling* or toy play. You'll want to start to integrate more personal interactions in your training though.

How to Play the Game:

Step 1: To start, engage your dog in personal interaction. This can be petting or a saying sweet things, or drawing your dog into you with some subtle movement. Begin to move in a way that draws your dog towards you. For some dogs you may need to be a little more active to start, more in line with the *Heel with Me! Play with Me!* game, before lowering your energy level. A quick game of chase (your dog chasing you) can help to jump start the exercise.

Step 2: Turn away from your dog and move forward. As your dog moves in alongside you, mark and reward. Ideally, you will reward with more personal play and interaction. If your dog is not yet ready for that, you can follow it up with *Jump to Food* or other construct game.

Allow your dog to offer coming into position – though if you feel they don't have enough information to come into your side, you can provide a physical cue such as your hand at your waist for obedience or your hand at your hip for freestyle. Presenting your hand for *Jump to Hand* and the start of the *Jump for Joy* game can give the dog the information they need that a heeling game is starting!

Keep the ratio of play to heeling high to start, gradually increasing the amount of heeling before going back to play.

Get Up and Go

In this exercise, we are going to use your dog's natural physical response or resistance to pressure to create energy and drive forward and up.

You will want to test their response to pressure first, as not all dogs enjoy this game. If your dog struggles with it, you don't have to include it in your repertoire of games.

How to Play the Game:

Step 1: To test your dog's response to physical pressure, sit on the floor with your dog and engage in a little play (if you have a larger breed dog you can do this standing up). Then play a little game of push-away by placing your open hand on your dog's chest or shoulder and gently pushing them away. Very gently - this should not be a shove, but just a little pressure away from you.

Will they come back? A little harder even? Do you feel pressure against your hand as you try to push your dog away? Do you see something that says they want to get at you even more? Or do they shy away from this, maybe even choosing not to engage? If the latter, do not move on to step 2. Choose a different game. Not all games are meant for all dogs. We must take the dog's preferences into account. Not all dogs will enjoy this game. There are plenty of other games to choose from!

If the former – and your dog seems to really get more into the game when you occasionally push them away, then you can proceed with the exercise.

Step 2: With your dog next to you, and both of you facing the same direction, bend, and using your hand closest to them put a little pressure against their chest, pushing them back slightly, then give your heel cue and move forward quickly. Be sure to preface this with a little game of push away to ensure your dog wants to play! When your dog comes into a nice position with head up, mark, hand touch and jump to food or toy! Then play and start again!

Turn 'n' Touch

It's not unusual for dogs to get a little flat, or lose animation on inside turns. They need to both actively slow in order to stay in position, as well as navigate the turn. This can create a lowering of the head, or moving from a trot into a walk. For this exercise, we are going to create a catalyst for the dog to engage their rear and lift up on the inside turn.

How to Play the Game:

Step 1: With your dog on the inside (on your left for left turns or on your right for right turns), start with a "soft" turn – a more curved or rounded turn rather than a 90-degree turn. You can do this by working in a loose oval. As you move through the turn, with your dog on the inside present your hand for *Jump to Hand*, mark, continue for a couple of steps through the turn as you get your treat, and have your dog *Jump for Food*. Once your dog is showing some lift moving through the turn and anticipation of the hand touch, we can add a little difficulty.

Step 2: Next, we'll tighten the turn. This is a more advanced skill so don't rush to this! It may take several sessions before you and your dog are ready for the tighter turn. As you prepare to step into the 90-degree turn, present your hand, mark the lift, continue through the turn then have your dog jump for food. If your dog struggles a little with the harder turn, continue with softer turns, gradually increasing the angle to 90 degrees.

Turn 'n' Toss

When dogs are on the outside of a turn they need to speed up if they are to stay in position. *Food Bowling* is an easy way to build anticipation and therefore speed around the turn.

How to Play the Game:

Step 1: With your dog on your left, heel in a loose 360-degree circle with your dog on the outside. Mark as you go into the turn, and your dog is alongside of you. Then as you get

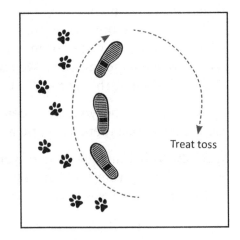

Treat toss

your treat out, finish the turn and bowl in the direction you are turning. You want your dog to continue across you to chase the treat.

Step 2: As your dog starts to get animated on the turn in anticipation of *Food Bowling*, you can move further into the turn before marking and then bowling again in the direction of the turn. You can use a cone to go around and create your circle. You want to start with a bit larger circle and gradually tighten your circle until it replicates a 90 or 180-degree turn. And don't get dizzy! Remember dogs can get dizzy too!

Out and Around Figure-8s

Some of you will look at this exercise and immediately think "oh, we are doing an obedience figure-8 exercise." Yes, we are using two cones, and yes this will benefit your figure-8 exercise. No, this is not an obedience figure-8 exercise! This game is all about variety and choices and creating a game that's all your own.

Using the construct games and other games, you will put them together into a fun game unique to you and your dog! Whatever game your dog loves, you can include it here!

The cones will "ground" the exercise and help define your path. Your path might be in the form of a figure-8, or it could be in an oval around both cones, or a 360-degree circle around a single cone, or any combination. Mix it up a bit!

If your dog likes *Food Bowling*, then be sure to include it! If they love going around a cone, do lots of *Catch Me If You Cone!* If they enjoy the *Turn 'n' Toss* or *Turn 'n' Touch* games, you can include those!

> "I am loving that our 'training' and 'play' sessions are getting more and more blurred!"
> ~ Angela and Eevee

The goal is to include both straight lines and curved lines while heeling and interject the games as reinforcement and respite.

How to Play the Game:

Step 1: Place 2 cones (or other standards) approximately 10-15 feet apart. It helps to have a plan the first few times you play the game, so consider practicing the different lines of travel you can take without your dog, and where you might include your games.

Step 2: Start the game with a bit of *Food Bowling*. Turn and begin to heel forward as your dog moves into position. Follow your planned path in and around the cones. Insert your first game after just a few steps! Provide a fun reward event that includes *Jump for Joy, Food Bowling,* and/or *Out and Around a Cone,* or even a bit of *Heel with Me! Play with Me!*

Step 3: Restart the game after bowling a treat or sending your dog around a cone.

It can help to keep a list of which activities and games your dog seems to really enjoy and which you want to put more value into. For this exercise, use the games your dog really enjoys.

While this game sounds easy, due to its fast pace, it's easy to lose your rhythm. *Food Bowling* is your friend here. It can reset the dog, allow for added fun and give you time to set up for your next move.

Notes:

CHAPTER 14:
More Games and Exercises for Precision Criteria

It can be easy to work the games that focus on our dog's emotional state more frequently than the games and exercises that target precision criteria, or alternately to spend too much time on precision exercises. Your goal is always to balance out your precision exercises with your "joy games" in a way that each benefits the other. The end result is a dog that chooses to put these two seemingly opposite criteria together on their own.

Sit Down Sit Stand Down Stand

Practicing position changes of sit, down, and stand in a specific order allows your dog to learn to remain in heel position while transitioning into other position behaviors. It has the added benefit of strengthening the muscle groups associated with each action.

Using props such as platforms or training gates, helps create and maintain precision and a pattern of accuracy as your dog moves through the behavior changes in relation to you. This exercise also allows you to practice your cue discrimination while maintaining heel position. Just a little added bonus!

Exercise: With your dog in heel position, cue your dog to perform the following behaviors, in this order, and mark and reward each correct response:

Sit – Down – Sit – Stand – Down – Stand

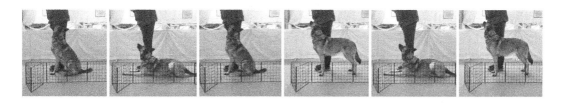

This specific order allows your dog to move into and out of each position, using the different muscle groups needed for each. Using *Jump for Joy* (*Jump to Hand/Jump to Food*) as reinforcement helps your dog learn to control their body in a way that they remain in position even with the added energy of jumping up between changes of positions.

This is more tiring than appears when your dog first starts working this exercise. So be sure to take plenty of breaks for *Food Bowling* or other games and keep your sessions short.

1-step Heel

This exercise allows you to provide a high rate of reward for the smallest piece of heeling – One step with lift. In many of the games, we used the dog's momentum to help build energy and lift. Now your dog will be working from a standstill and will need to create energy from stillness. If you actively train in obedience, you have probably worked this from a sit. You want to also work it from the stand.

Use the gates or other low barrier to maintain your dog's position as they lift up. This takes practice and muscle memory and often it is the energy and joy that we want that can create some loss of position, that we don't want! The gates remind the dog to work to stay in position.

This exercise also allows us to use our verbal heel cue, as we know that between the hand target for lift and the gate for straight, we will get the criteria included in the meaning of our cue.

How to Play the Game:

Step 1: Start with your dog standing in heel position, between you and the gates. Your dog should be close enough to the gates to stay straight though not so close that they are tentative or curl behind you. Give the heel cue you've been using with your platform exercises, *then* take a step forward as you bring your hand target up for *Jump to Hand*. Mark the touch and reward with a *Jump to Food*. Coming up for reward doubles down on reinforcing the lift.

The order is important: Cue heel, *then* take your step as you present your hand target. Your hand target is effectively creating the lift on the first step.

Step 2: When your dog is consistently stepping with you to *Jump to Hand*, **change the timing and order** of the presentation of your hand. Now, you will give your heel cue, *then* step, *then* present your hand. Your heel cue will predict your step, which allows your dog to stay with you. And your step now predicts your hand cue, which creates anticipation and lift.

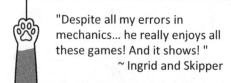

"Despite all my errors in mechanics... he really enjoys all these games! And it shows! "
~ Ingrid and Skipper

Following the reward, some dogs will need to drop their head to swallow. Be sure to wait to start the next rep until your dog's head is up and looking at you, telling you they are ready.

Once you and your dog are comfortable with the mechanics of the exercise, you can add in your other construct games such as *Food Bowling,* or *Out and Around* as resets and reward events after several reps.

Find Heel! Double Duty

This game provides double the fun and double the reinforcement for finding position. It can be played on or off cue, depending on your dog's skill at shaping and understanding of their position cue. It helps your dog learn how to find heel from both in front of you and from behind you.

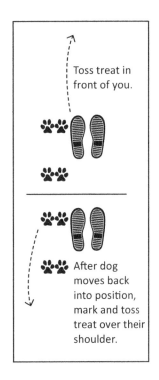

Toss treat in front of you.

After dog moves back into position, mark and toss treat over their shoulder.

How to Play the Game:

Step 1: Start with your dog standing in left or right heel position. Provide some *Fast Food*.

Step 2: Release your dog to a tossed treat in front of you. As your dog moves back to you and swings into position, mark and toss the treat over their shoulder and behind you.

Step 3: As your dog moves back - and eventually into - position from behind you, you can mark and toss forward again.

Step 4: Continue to shape to the full position. Then add your other criteria of eye contact and a bit of duration before starting your tosses again. If you or your dog struggle with shaping in this exercise, you can use the colored mats, platforms or gates to help jump start the game.

Quarter-turn Spins

This exercise encourages your dog to shift their rear into you and associate that action with your heel cue, as well as the start to some lateral work. Dogs seem to like to spin and if you've already taught it, spin likely has a strong reward history associated with it, so the spin itself can add some fun to this exercise for your dog. Be sure to reward generously with fun and games like *Food Bowling* or toy play to keep the energy up.

How to Play the Game:

Step 1: With your dog in heel, cue a spin. If your dog is in left heel, cue a counter-clockwise spin, and if your dog is in right heel cue a clockwise spin. You can use a hand cue or verbal cue, or if your dog does not know how to spin you can use a lure, later transferring to a hand cue.

Step 2: As your dog is at about the three-quarter point in the spin, give your heel position cue and make a 90-degree quarter turn toward your dog. You and your dog are now facing the same direction, 90 degrees from where you started. Mark as your dog comes into position and reward with *Fast Food* to build value in position and repeat.

The momentum of the spin can cause some over-rotation at times. If you are frequently getting over-rotation you may opt to not do this exercise, and instead, work a stationary spin with a standing platform to help your dog work to keep their rear straight and in line with you. Feeding with your opposite hand can also help to mitigate any over-rotating of your dog's rear behind you. Thankfully, the over-rotation doesn't tend to carry over into turns or moving heel, though we still want our dogs to understand where they should be or move to when we give our heel cue.

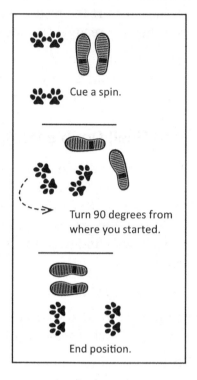

Cue a spin.

Turn 90 degrees from where you started.

End position.

Slide to side

This game uses a change of direction, without disconnecting from your dog, to encourage your dog to stay focused and attentive while heeling. It can also be used as a way to regain a loss of focus or position.

How to Play the Game:

Step 1: After a few steps of heeling, call your dog to you as you start to move backward quickly. Your dog should turn to face you, and start to move to and with you as you move backward. Your dog should be focused and attentive when moving to Step 2.

Step 2: After a few steps turn 180 degrees, now facing in the same direction as your dog, with your dog now in heel position.

After a few steps of heeling, present your hand for *Jump to Hand*, then *Jump to Food*, and start the game again.

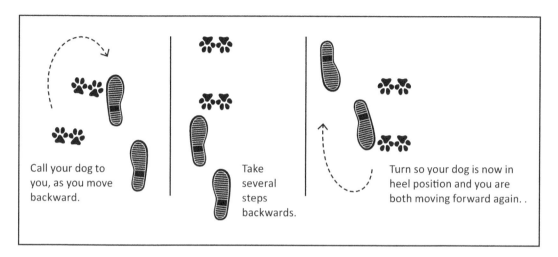

Call your dog to you, as you move backward.

Take several steps backwards.

Turn so your dog is now in heel position and you are both moving forward again. .

Rock-a-Bye Backs

This is an extension of your *1-step Heel* game and adds an additional direction of movement. The goal in heelwork is that your dog wants to stay at your leg, no matter where your leg goes - forward, pivot, back, or even sideways.

How to Play the Game:

Set up your training gates in a straight line so they are on the outside of your dog and your dog is between you and the gates. Again, be close enough to create a straight position, but not so close that your dog curls behind you. Provide a bit of *Fast Food* to build value in being at your leg with the gate on the outside.

Step 1: With your dog between you and the gates, give your heel cue and take a single step forward with your leg closest to your dog – your left leg if working on left heel and your right leg if working on right heel. Keep your opposite leg in place and planted. Only the leg closest to your dog will move.

You may need to prompt with a hand target or piece of food to start. Use the prompt judiciously and for not more than a couple of reps.

Mark as your dog moves with you. Reward without moving your legs. Your legs should be scissored at this point. Provide *Fast Food* in position.

Step 2: Following reward, rock and step back so that your leg moves back to in line with your far leg. Mark as your dog moves with you, and provide *Fast Food* in position. Your legs are now together.

Step 3: Then, with your leg closest, take another step back, keeping your far leg planted. Your dog is moving with your close leg. Mark and reward your dog for moving back with you.

Then step forward again to line up with your far leg. For each correct response, provide *Fast Food*.

With your far leg planted, the sequence of steps is:

- Step forward with close leg, mark, reward, *Fast Food*
- Step back with close leg so feet are now together, mark, reward, *Fast Food*
- Step back again with close leg, mark, reward, *Fast Food*
- Step forward close leg so feet are now together, mark, reward, *Fast Food*.

After a few reps, your dog should start to be able to move with your leg without aid or prompting. You can then add your verbal heel cue.

Stand By Me! Laterals and Sidepasses

Lateral work, sometimes referred to as a sidepass, is when the dog and handler are moving in unison, laterally, or sideways with the dog in a precise position.

In freestyle, sidepasses are performed with the dog in one of the four primary positions of left, right, center or behind or in one of the many "alternative" positions. Here we will just be working in left or right heel with the dog moving into the handler.

Moving laterally, or sidepassing in left and right heel helps build a strong understanding of the position as a constant, no matter the direction. The cue for a sidepass into you is the same as your left or right heel cue.

You will have done some stationary position work on a standing platform and introduced the cues for left heel and right heel. You then added the pivot platforms to create a better understanding of the verbal cue and the value of rear-end awareness adding movement. The dog had to "seek out" heel position, as the handler moved away from the dog.

Once the dog is on the flat, no longer on the pivot platform, we have a wider range of movement we can start to introduce to the dog. We introduced moving forward with *1-step Heel* and moving backward with the *Rock-a-Bye Backs*. The goal is always the same - stay in position in relation to the handler, no matter what direction the handler moves.

The sidepass is really just a pivot (90-degree inside turn) that has been "flattened." The pivot is a corner (90 degrees), and the sidepass is a straight line (0 degrees). The transition between the two is a curve or arch (45 degrees). To train the sidepass you'll change your footwork and the angle of your turn but keep the same heelwork cue.

It's important that your dog has a strong pivot on the flat to get the most out of the below exercises and create your sidepasses. If you are still working on getting pivots on the flat, continue with that. There is no rush to move into sidepasses. The goal is all the same: building value in being next to you in position.

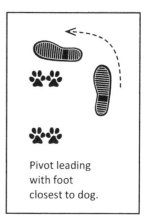

Pivot leading with foot closest to dog.

Lead with opposite foot.

Exercise:

Step 1: Start with your dog in either left or right heel. Choose your dog's strongest side to start. Give the position cue, then perform a 90-degree pivot, just as you would if on the pivot platform, leading with the foot closest to your dog. Repeat 2-4 times to ensure criteria is met. Mark and reward and provide a little *Fast Food* for each rep.

Step 2: Once your dog is consistently successful at the 90-degree pivots, on the next rep, lead with your far foot and step away from your dog on a curve as if stepping around a hoop or large bowl with your toes in toward the edge. You and your dog are now moving at a 45-degree angle, rather than a 90-degree angle.

Take a small step away from your dog.

Be sure your step is small. The biggest mistake handlers make here is taking too large of a step. Take one step, and mark and reward any movement into you, no matter how small. Then, if need be, move nearer to your dog so you are both facing forward.Provide *Fast Food* to build value there.

Step 3: On the next rep, perform a 90-degree pivot again, just as you did in step 1. Mark and reward your dog moving into heel.

Provide *Fast Food* with each rep where your dog is fully in position. This will continue to build value in staying close to you, especially if your dog is struggling.

Step 4: On the next few reps, alternate between your 90-degree pivots and your curved or 45-degree step, until your dog is working hard to stay with you on the curve. It's important to alternate with the easier and better-known pivot to maintain a high level of success and confidence as you make the behavior harder by flattening out the curve.

Step 5: As your dog starts to show confidence, raise your criteria following a pivot step, and take a small, straight, lateral step away from your dog. Mark and reward generously, then return to alternating between your 90-degree, 45-degree and lateral step.

If your dog starts to lead with their front feet, then catch up with their rear when moving into a straight sidepass, your steps are likely too large. We overestimate the ability of our dogs to step wide laterally. Think of how narrow their chest is. Their front legs are attached to that and they don't have the lateral flexibility that we do with our legs and hips. So take smaller steps than you think you need to.

We Don't Need No Stinkin' Heeling!

When training the behavior of heeling, it's normal to want to actually do some heeling! All to often though we tend to focus on "moving in heel with duration" before laying the groundwork for what we want that to look like. In my early days of attending obedience classes, we "practiced heeling" by moving around in a big circle, hoping our dogs were where they should be.

You can practice something ad infinitum, but all that time spent practicing won't benefit you unless what you are practicing is what you really want. Building the individual components of heeling before putting it all together is the difference between a dog with full understanding and enjoyment of heelwork and the dog that lacks confidence, precision, or accuracy.

By breaking out the pieces that make up beautiful and joyful heelwork and training them separately, we allow the dog, through a history of reinforcement and enjoyment, to bring these pieces together. The result is a naturalness and fluidity of the movement and the outward expression of joy that comes from confidence and the expectation of a positive outcome. This is what Joy of Heeling is all about.

For several sessions after your dog is successful with their first lateral steps, alternate between pivots (90 degrees) and the curve (45 degrees) and your sidepass or lateral step (0 degrees). Whenever your dog struggles, go back to the familiar pivot and reward generously in position.

While you want to have strong pivots on the flat before working your sidepasses exercise with your dog, you can practice your footwork any time!

More Lateral Exercises

The above exercise uses the value you have built into your heel position to create the sidepass. The exercises below use your dog's momentum to carry them into the sidepass with greater ease, providing an opportunity for you to mark and reward for moving into you laterally with energy.

This first exercise is an extension of your *Quarter-turn Spins* exercise.

Step 1: Warm up with a couple of *Quarter-turn Spins*.

Step 2: With your dog next to you in heel position, cue your dog to spin. As your dog executes the spin, and as they are just about back into heel position, rather than turn 90 degrees, give your heel cue and take a small step away from them laterally. Mark and reward your dog's effort moving into you to get to heel position. Provide *Fast Food* and repeat.

Who's got the Corkscrew?

There are 2 variations of this exercise:

In the first, you and your dog are going to heel forward moving in a wide circle, about 10-12 feet in diameter. With your dog on the inside, spiral the circle smaller and smaller until your dog is pivoting next to you.

Then from the pivot start to open up your circle and straighten out the curve so that your dog is now taking a few steps of sidepasses. Be sure to mark after just a couple of steps to start before building more duration.

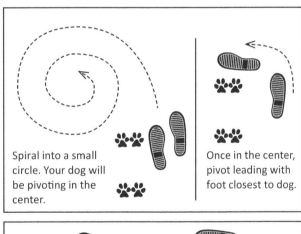

Spiral into a small circle. Your dog will be pivoting in the center.

Once in the center, pivot leading with foot closest to dog.

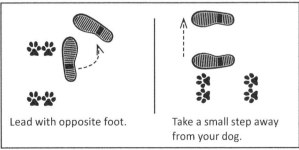

Lead with opposite foot.

Take a small step away from your dog.

The second variation is similar to the first in that it starts the same way with you and your dog heeling forward into a spiral with your dog on the inside. Once your spiral is small enough to pivot, you will start to widen your pivot into the spiral moving out from the center, making it larger and larger but in a lateral movement with your dog.

1-Step, 2-step, 3-step, More! Multi-directional Heelwork

This exercise can really increase your dog's focus in your heelwork and they often seem to enjoy this bit of a challenge.

It is exactly as it sounds. One step at a time, you will give your heel cue, then take a single step in a different direction. Mark and reward generously, each correct response of your dog moving with you. Work to reward your dog in position even if you need to create it by stepping to your dog.

The only direction you will *not* step is *into* your dog. This is asking your dog to move away from you and out of position. Each step you take should encourage your dog to move into you and stay at your leg: forward, backward, away from your dog, and both forward and back pivots.

Be generous with your rewards. This is harder than it sounds and it will be important to maintain value in position, without the aid of props.

Notes:

_____

_____

_____

_____

_____

_____

_____

_____

_____

_____

_____

_____

_____

_____

_____

_____

_____

_____

_____

_____

PART V

Developing Grit

Games, Resilience, Integration, Teamwork

CHAPTER 15:
Distractions and Duration

Part of the process of training, whether teaching manners or competition behaviors is teaching our dogs how to execute trained behaviors in difficult settings or environments. And like all training, this should be done incrementally, allowing the dog to drive the process.

Green Eggs and Ham: Over Easy, Over Hard

You may have heard of the "Green Eggs and Ham" proofing exercise where you "ask" progressively harder questions starting with "Can you do it if....." You are setting the dog up in various scenarios to see if they can succeed when there is added difficulty. While this is a good way to check your dog's understanding of a skill and increase their proficiency, it can easily backfire if you push too hard, or ask for too much for too long. Frustration or confusion can be the result. Joy is the opposite of these feelings or emotions.

As we add duration, distractions and other challenges such as more difficult environments, the goal is to work our dogs in a way that success is attainable, that the task is still doable even with the added difficulty. Aim for just enough challenge so that your dog must focus on succeeding at the task but not so challenging that there are numerous failures, creating a lack of confidence, disengagement or frustration. Ideally, the little bit of challenge not only increases focus on the task but also teaches the value in persistence as it results in longer-lasting reward events, more games and more joy!

"Heeling is hard by itself... I know we think we know that. But as soon as we add duration or difficulty in the form of distractions our dogs can lose confidence in their heelwork. Too much difficulty added to an already difficult task of heeling will create a loss of confidence and criteria."

Working in a structured way, sticking to the rule of "easy hard easy hard" or "ping-ponging" between the added difficulty, then back to something easier, ensures that our dogs are winning much of the time and earning relief from pressure as part of reinforcement. The eventuality is that the "Hard" then becomes "Easy" and we can add more variety and other layers of "Hard."

The experience and reward history of added challenges to the games is what allows us to continue to expand on our dog's skill, maintaining enthusiasm, animation, and joy in the task of heeling. Winning at challenges creates confidence and allows our dogs to learn about perseverance in the presence of added difficulty. You might find that this can bring a bit of spark to your dog in their efforts to push past the challenge!

Gutter balls

We all know that in bowling not only do we want to hit as many pins as we can, but we also want to keep the ball out of the gutter! The "gutter" is the stimuli or attractions that our dogs can become distracted by. I want my dog's mind to stay out of the gutter!

In this game, we start to add a bit more difficulty/distractions to our *Food Bowling/ Jump for Joy* games. As with all the games, the goal is to gradually extend the number of steps of animated heeling.

Start small, and as your dog succeeds, increase the number of steps.

Then alternate between easy-hard-easy-hard. Whether you choose to change the intensity or proximity of the distraction or change the number of steps you can adjust the added difficulty to give respite and make it easier, or push their skill up to doable difficulty and make it harder.

Think of this as another chapter to your *Treats on a Seat Game.* You can start with *Treats on a Seat* as a warm-up if you like.

How to Play the Game:

Step 1: Place several treats in a partially enclosed container. Your dog should be able to see and smell them,

> ### Distractions Lead to Games and Games Lead to Heeling
>
> *When increasing difficulty, adding an active game such as Food Bowling and* Jump for Joy *or* Catch Me if You Cone, *can both relieve pressure and help to create a predictable pattern. The active game that leads into heelwork predicts focused heeling. The added difficulty or distraction we have set up predicts a game, which then predicts focused heeling. That's a bit different from the way we generally think of "proofing."*

but not get to them. A plastic container will work well. You can poke holes in it to make it a little bit enticing. Place it on a chair or table or what you used for the *Treats on a Seat* game.

Step 2: Start a game of *Food Bowling* past the container of food. You can also opt to use a toy or anything your dog might be drawn to in place of the food. You want to ensure that the attraction is inaccessible and not available to your dog if he goes to investigate.

After a few reps of *Food Bowling*, add your *Jump for Joy* exercise moving forward as your dog is behind you getting the bowled treat. Present your hand target, as your dog comes into position, mark, then *Jump to Food*, then bowl again past the attraction.

To increase difficulty, you can either increase the value or proximity of the attraction or increase your duration in the number of steps. But not both at the same time. For example, adding a person can replicate a judge or steward in the ring, or changing the location of the attraction from the chair to the floor, or adding multiple attractions. Even the distance or proximity in which you bowl your treat will affect the difficulty level for your dog.

If your dog moves to the attraction, call him back and start your *Food Bowling* and *Jump for Joy* again, albeit with a bit more distance. If your dog moves to the attraction more than a couple of times, even after at more distance, lower the value of the attraction and increase the value of your reinforcement.

Make sure that when you are increasing the value or intensity of the attraction/distraction, that you are also decreasing the duration in the number of steps you are asking of your dog.

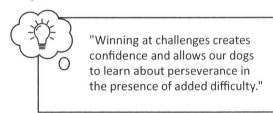

"Winning at challenges creates confidence and allows our dogs to learn about perseverance in the presence of added difficulty."

Chews to Heel

This is loosely based on a protocol developed by Dawn Jecs called "Choose to Heel©." My version is slightly different. In general, it is absent of cues and allows the dog to learn that by seeking out proximity to the handler, rewards happen. It is a shaping protocol that eventually builds to precision, accuracy, and duration in heelwork.

You'll want a bit of larger space for this as you will be moving in a large circle.

How to Play the Game

Step 1: Start by "priming the pump." By that, I mean letting the dog know that rewards are available for being close to you.

Drop a few treats on the ground. As your dog is eating the treats, walk a few steps away. When your dog finishes the treats and moves close to you, mark and drop a few more treats. Repeat a couple of times until your dog is immediately moving to you after eating the treats.

Be sure that when you move away your back is to your dog.

Step 2: After dropping your treats, start to move out at a slightly quicker pace. Don't wait for your dog to finish eating the treats. Let him seek you out. When he starts to get closer, mark, *Jump for Joy,* (*Jump to Hand/Jump to Food*), then put a few more treats on the ground, and start walking forward again.

Step 3: Continue with step 2, gradually increasing your criteria of position and attention.

Step 4: Add duration by adding steps while maintaining position, before marking or *Jump to Hand*. Reward with treats on the ground to start the next rep or provide a reward event.

If you are working both left and right heel, when moving in the circle in left heel, move counter-clockwise. If working right heel, move in a clockwise direction. The dog should be on the inside of the circle. You can also work this in a straight line.

If you only work the left side, heel your dog on the outside of the circle, moving in a clockwise direction.

Initially, your dog does not need to be in heel position to earn reward. You need to determine what criteria your dog can easily achieve in terms of proximity and then shape closer proximity from there.

Mark frequently at the start. If you are walking more than 6 or so steps in your first few reps, you are asking for too much. If your dog appears confused or worried about this, make it easier by either encouraging them closer to you for reward or mark sooner - before they are as close as you'd like but still moving in your direction. Provide a greater value and quantity of rewards for this exercise than you think you need. And don't make assumptions about what your dog "knows." Make this easy to start.

"Disengagement gives you information about your dog's level of confidence and commitment. You don't want to work a dog that is not committed to the session."

Try not to look back for your dog. If you really aren't sure where they are, take a quick glance but try to maintain a forward posture for this exercise. Work toward keeping a consistent pace and not slow down as your dog catches up. When you mark, keep moving a couple of steps forward as you present your hand and get your treat out so there is no abrupt stop to movement.

Choose Me!

This game combines *Gutter Balls* with the *Chews to Heel game* In the Gutter Balls game, we introduced the concept of ignoring distractions using *Food Bowling* and *Jump for Joy* (*Jump to Hand/Jump to Food*). That game allowed us to assess and increase our dog's ability to maintain the games while heeling with the added difficulty of an attraction, such as food or toys.

Step 1: Start with a game of *Gutter Balls* including some heeling and *Jump for Joy*. Instead of a single attraction, such as a container of food or a single toy, place one or two additional attractions, spaced well apart. The attractions can be neutral or low value to start, such as an empty bucket or a less favored toy.

Step 2: As your dog finishes eating a bowled treat, instead of bowling again, start walking briskly in various lines of travel through and around the items laying on the floor. As your dog moves toward you and alongside you as in the *Chews to Heel* game, mark and reward with *Jump for Joy* (*Jump to Hand/Jump to Food*). Bowl another piece of food and repeat. The goal is not to try to lose your dog, but rather to build his confidence in distracting environments and teach him that choosing you yields the most reinforcement.

Step 3: Increase the number or value of the attractions. Be sure to also increase your reward event either in duration or value.

If your dog struggles, reduce the number or value of the additional attractions and increase your rate or value of the reward, or go back to the foundation games of *Gutter Balls, Heel with Me! Play with Me!* and *Just Do It!*

Building Duration: Hand Targets, Ping-Pong and Heeling Grids

One of the most difficult aspects of heeling is building duration while keeping the joy. In using the games, we can build value and excitement in positioning and focus and help to create a dog and handler team that looks forward to heelwork rather than dreading it. Adding duration and keeping that joy seems to be where many struggle.

We tend to reward after about the same number of steps. When we do increase our duration, we often ask for too much and often start to see a decrease in that animation and joy we have worked to build. We often end up rewarding "less than" execution just to help build back confidence. There are several ways to add duration to your heelwork and still maintain that animation you have been building.

Teaching duration in any skill is about teaching the dog to "do it until..." That could be a marker, a release cue or another behavior cue. In essence, we want our dog to continue until we tell them to do something else. When we use a marker or secondary reinforcer following an interval of heeling, we are reinforcing the duration, and anything else that occurred during that duration.

In building duration, or extending the time working while decreasing the rate of reward, we can use the anticipation of reward to maintain attitude and a desire to continue the behavior.

To do that though, our dogs need to believe that reward is going to happen. We want our dogs to believe that reward is coming, and we want them to not worry if it takes a little bit of time.

A dog that understands duration in other behaviors has an easier time understanding heeling as a duration skill. So before having an expectation that your dog is able to heel for longer periods of time, be sure your dog has experience of duration with other behaviors such as long sits or downs, or short sequences of behaviors.

Using a Hand Target to Build Duration

The cool thing is that we have already started communicating duration through our *Jump to Hand* game! When you present your hand, you are indicating the end of the duration. Your hand acts as a secondary reinforcer or marker, and your *Jump to Food* and *Food Bowling* and other games, act as your primary reinforcer.

By extending the time before presenting our hand, we are building in the format of a mini behavior chain, which includes heeling, our games and reward event and back to heeling. We are able to add duration in the first behavior in the chain, which is heeling. Our dog is learning to "do it until..." the hand is presented. Animation is maintained as our dog anticipates the appearance of the hand target, which starts the reward event (*Jump to Food, Food Bowling*, tug etc.). Pretty slick!

Having clear criteria when adding duration is what defines success.

Just as we present our hand target to indicate the end of duration and the start of reinforcement, strategically withholding your marker (whether a click or "yes" or other marker) builds duration in heelwork. It is virtually identical to the way we build duration in our other trained behaviors.

If I want to build duration in a sit, for example, I start by marking and rewarding just the act of sitting. I would then add a small amount of duration - say 1 second - before marking and rewarding at the end of that short duration. After a few reps I would increase to 2-3 seconds. The dog is learning to "do it until..." the marker, (eventually transitioned to a release cue) which starts the reward event. I could then continue to build or shape my duration in small increments or successive approximations.

By using a hand target as a marker, indicating success and the end of the duration of heeling, we can create not only lift in anticipation of when the hand may appear over-head, but clear and consistent communication of "continue until you see my hand appear." Providing both a visual and a tactile marker helps to maintain your dog's focus and position.

Ping-ponging uses the concept of "easy-hard-easy" to build duration without making it too difficult all at once. Adding too much duration at once can result in a dog that loses confidence or a loss of quality of behavior. When ping-ponging, the relief of pressure acts as reinforcement for the harder reps.

Below is an example of ping-ponging the criterion of the number of steps of heeling in a session. Each rep in which the dog maintained that criterion is reinforced. You can see the pattern of easy-hard-easy-hard.

Session	
Rep	**Steps**
Rep 1	6
Rep 2	10
Rep 3	5
Rep 4	12
Rep 5	8
Rep 6	15

In 6 reps of heeling, we've more than doubled the duration, from 6 steps to 15. Providing a higher quality of reward event for more steps, can increase your dog's desire to continue to work toward more duration

So while you might give a hand touch and a single treat for heeling 6 steps, by the time you get up to 15 steps you will have incrementally increased your reward event for more difficult reps to include *Jump to Food, Food Bowling* a couple of times and a fun game of tug, chase or fetch for the longest duration. The harder or longer you ask your dog to work, the higher the quality or quantity of the reward. Think of this as minimum wage versus living wage, versus abundance in both wages and enjoyment of the work! Heeling is hard! No dog will continue to work hard for minimum wage.

Ping-ponging and using our hand touch and other games at the end of a set of reps is a means to increase the duration of heelwork while maintaining attitude and enthusiasm. It is a structured way to reduce reinforcement without losing a willingness to keep working.

Heeling grids are similar to **ping-ponging** in that both are based on using a variable number of steps that are also progressive. I was introduced to heeling grids by Laura Romanik. In heeling grids, each session has a specific minimum and maximum number of steps. It is the sessions themselves that increase in duration. Laura offers a training log that provides a structured format of heeling grids to increase the duration of your heeling while maintaining enthusiasm. I highly recommend it for keeping track of your progress (check the resources section for how to order her log book)

Below is an example of a couple of heeling grid sessions showing the increase in the number of steps of heeling.

Session 1			
Set	**Number of steps**		
Set 1	2	6	4	10
Set 2	6	4	10	2
Set 3	4	10	2	6
Set 4	10	2	6	4

Session 2			
Set	**Number of steps**		
Set 1	5	8	10	16
Set 2	8	10	16	5
Set 3	10	16	5	8
Set 4	16	5	8	10

Each new session increases the highest number of steps in each repetition, while also maintaining much easier reps, creating an upward progression in duration while maintaining accuracy and animation using the easy-hard-easy-hard rule. Be sure to reward after each rep in a set. Your reward should be commensurate with the amount of duration you are asking for.

Notes:

_____

_____

_____

_____

_____

_____

_____

_____

_____

_____

_____

_____

_____

_____

_____

_____

_____

_____

_____

_____

CHAPTER 16

Fix it! Using Tricks and Games to Troubleshoot

You may find that there are certain criteria where your dog might need a bit of a refresher or that you would like to further improve upon. It's not unusual to have some criteria diminish while we are building other criteria. Criteria that are reinforced will increase and those criteria that are not being reinforced at that same rate can diminish.

When using props, such as the standing platform, pivot platform and training gates, we can clearly define to the dog where their body should be in relation to the handler. Through patterning or muscle memory, our reinforcement strategies, and the process of removing the props, there is a high degree of success in maintaining our position criteria. In the absence of these aids, or when adding movement, our dogs must work harder, both mentally and physically to maintain the patterns taught with the aids.

As previously noted, one of the most important components of heelwork is rear-end awareness - the dog being aware of where their rear is and where it should be. We build this awareness in several ways: through our pivot work, teaching backing, and lateral work. There are ways to use our dog's natural movement and momentum to fix issues, such as lagging, forging, or crabbing, while keeping it fun and motivating. And that's where tricks come in, specifically spins, circling the handler, and passing through the handler's legs.

Your dog doesn't need to have these behaviors on verbal cues before you can start to use them. A hand cue is fine. Most dogs catch on to these behaviors quickly with a lure and transfer them to a hand signal. You do want to spend a little time building a reward history and understanding of the basic skill. It's best for these behaviors to already evoke an HER in your dog.

If you are a freestyler, you'll want to take the time to teach the verbal cues and include the criteria of a start and end position. If you are an obedience exhibitor, teaching your dog that these behaviors include the specific criteria of start and end positions will greatly benefit their desire to get to and stay in heel position, due to the increased reward history.

Quarter-turn Spin: On the Move!

Previously, I've talked about a couple of different exercises to increase both lift and accurate position for turns. In the *Turn 'n' Touch* game for inside turns, we used a *Jump to Hand* during the turn to create lift and in the *Quarter-turn Spins* we had the dog spin out away from us as we turned in the direction of the dog and gave our heel cue, using the dog's momentum to aid in coming fully back into position. Next, we are going to add movement to our *Quarter-turn Spins*.

How to Play the Game:

Step 1: Warm up with a couple of stationary *Quarter-turn Spins*. Mark coming into position and reward with *Fast Food*.

Step 2: Start by taking a few steps with your dog in heel while moving in a wide arc or circle. Your dog will be on the inside of the curve. If you are moving counter-clockwise your dog will be on your left. If you are moving clockwise your dog will be on your right.

Step 3: Cue the spin – you can use a hand cue if your dog does not have a verbal spin cue – and mark coming back to heel. If your dog is lagging slightly, it's more than likely due to you forging! When your dog spins, he is not moving forward. Be sure to pause or slow your step every so slightly to allow your dog to complete the spin and move back into position. Continue moving forward on the curve as you get your treat out. Reward with a *Jump to Food*.

The purpose of using the spin on the turns is to utilize the dog's natural momentum of their rear end to bring them into a tighter heel position. They will also need to work to push with their rear as they work to make the turn. Many dogs will start to lift their front feet off the ground as they turn into the spin. To me, this always looks as if the dog is truly enjoying this particular exercise.

Circle Turns for Forging or Lagging

We can use the circle behavior (the dog going around the handler in a circle) on the outside turns to help resolve both lagging and forging on the turn depending on the location of our reward delivery.

If your dog tends to lag on outside turns, you can use the circle behavior combined with *Food Bowling* to encourage your dog to drive forward and across you on the turn.

As the dog comes to expect where and how the reward will be delivered, they will start to drive around the handler in anticipation of a bowled treat, providing the opportunity to mark driving forward on the turn.

Be sure to warm up with a couple of stationary circles first. Reward the circle by bowling a treat across your body using your left hand if your dog is on your left and your right hand if your dog is on your right.

How to Play the Game:

Step 1: Begin by heeling forward into a slight curve with your dog on the outside of the curve. If your dog is on your left you will move clockwise. If your dog is on your right you will move counter-clockwise.

As you turn into the curve, cue your dog to circle, or go around you. Again, you can use a hand cue or a verbal cue. You will need to pause your forward movement to allow your dog to circle you.

As your dog completes the full 360-degree circle, and before he stops, toss a treat across your body for your dog to chase.

If you are late, and you think he will stop before you are able to toss the treat, turn in a tight forward pivot before bowling the treat.

Step 2: After a few reps, as you see your dog start to anticipate the circle cue and treat toss by driving forward or working hard to stay with you on the turn, mark and follow up with a treat toss across your body.

Step 3: Begin to tighten your path so it is less of a curve and more of a rounded 90-degree turn. Repeat as above.

Forging, Lagging and more!

Each venue or titling organization has a standardized heel position that is defined in their rules.

If you are new to heelwork, some terms may be unfamiliar to you.

The following refer to the accuracy of position.

Forging: *If the dog is forging, they are forward of the desired position.*

Lagging: *If the dog is lagging, they are behind the desired position*

Crabbing: *If the dog is crabbing, then their rear is angled out away from the handler*

Crowding: *If the dog is crowding, then they are moving into the handler in a way that impedes the handler's movement.*

Drifting: *When drifting, the handler is not moving in a straight line and is either moving slightly away from the dog or slightly into the dog.*

While forging on an outside turn tends to be less likely, some dogs start to forge as a result of some of the games.

If your dog tends to forge on the outside turn, instead of tossing the treat as above, have your dog come up to a hand touch as in the *Jump for Joy* game.

This transfers their energy from driving forward, to driving upward, creating both lift and accuracy of position. The anticipation of the presentation of your hand will encourage your dog to work to stay in position.

Step 1: Begin by heeling forward on a slight curve with your dog on the outside of the curve. If your dog is on your left you will move clockwise. If your dog is on your right you will move counter-clockwise.

As you move through the curve, present your hand in line with your hip then provide your reward with *Jump to Food*. Be sure your hand is not forward of your body. You want your dog to move upward, not forward. The anticipation of your hand target and its specific location will cause your dog to work hard to stay in line with your hip rather than moving ahead.

Your hand position is what makes this game successful in mitigating forging on the outside turn and gives your dog an outlet for the energy we want to maintain. If you find your dog is still forging after a few sessions, change the location of your treats to your back pocket or shift your bait bag behind you.

Step 2: Begin to tighten your path so it is less of a curve and more of a rounded 90-degree turn. Repeat as in Step 1

As with the previous circle game for lagging, your dog will start to anticipate the location of the presentation of your hand, giving you an opportunity to mark the correct position on the turn.

Working both of these "circle turn" games can help to head off any inconsistency in position on the turns.

Slide on Through!

This is a fun and quick game that many dogs find lots of joy in! It can also be very effective in maintaining positions on both inside and outside turns.

Before playing this game, be sure your dog has a strong reward history for both going through your leg and a hand touch.

"If we are playing the games in a way that our dog is flat, then we are associating a flat demeanor with the games and heeling. Sometimes it's better not to play some games if the conditions aren't right."

How to Play the Game:

Step 1: Start with your dog in front of you. Encourage your dog through your leg and into position. As your dog comes into position, present your hand for *Jump to Hand* then follow up with *Jump to Food*.

When your dog is showing confidence in the pattern, move on to Step 2.

Step 2: Bowl a treat in front of you for your dog to chase, creating a bit of distance between you and your dog. You can also send your dog *Out and Around* a cone to gain distance. As your dog moves back to you, encourage a bit of speed by calling them to you or by praising or moving backward.

As your dog approaches you, cue them to go through your forward leg (left leg for your dog to go through to your left, and right leg if you want your dog to go through to your right) encouraging them into position. If using your position cue, be sure to give it as your dog is going through your leg, not after. Again, you want them to move directly into position upon passing through your legs.

As your dog passes through your leg and moves into position, take a step forward and present your hand target at your hip. Mark and reward the *Jump to Hand* with a *Jump to Food*.

Step 3: Repeat as above, alternating between taking 1-2 steps forward before *Jump to Hand, Jump to Food*, and then taking several steps forward for *Jump to Hand, Jump to Food*. In other words, ping-pong your duration, ending with *Jump for Joy, Food Bowling* or *Out and Around a Cone* then starting the game again!

Having your dog move through your legs and into position, followed immediately with a *Jump to Hand* will help build lift and push from the rear on the straight and on outside turns.

Pop Up!

This game is an extension of your *1-step Heel* exercise. It gives your dog a reason to pop out of their sit and start heeling with enthusiasm and can be used to mitigate issues with the head dropping on the first step.

How to Play the Game:

Step 1: Start with your dog in a sit beside Don't ask your dog to come to heel. Instead ask them to sit and then you move to stand next to them. This exercise is not about setting up the dog in a sit in heel..

Ask your dog for a *Jump to Hand* with your hand just over your dog's head so they need to push up to touch it. Mark the touch, *Jump to Food* as reward. Be sure to warm up with some touches beforehand.

This is not an easy thing to do and even if your dog has strong touches, they may hesitate or not be able to pop up. Make it easy to start – keep your hand low. Even start with having your dog *Jump to Food* if needed. We don't want our dogs to get frustrated about not getting up to the hand.

Step 2: After a couple of successful stationary reps as above, give your heel cue first, then take a step forward. At the same time as you step forward, bring your hand up for a hand touch. Mark the touch, then jump to reward.

When your dog is consistently popping up to touch your hand as you step, change the timing and order of your step and hand presentation to stepping first, then presenting the hand. This allows the dog to start to anticipate the hand touch and lift up on that first step without the visual of your hand. If you are providing a verbal heel cue, that should preface any movement from you.

This is a hard skill for many dogs. If you doubt it, sit in a chair with your hips and rear all the way back in the seat, place your feet flat on the floor, put your arms up with your palms toward the ceiling, and look straight up toward your hands. Now without bringing your arms or head down or bending at the waist, stand up. You'll find it's not such an easy task.

Slow Dancing... and Boogie!

This fun and active game gives your dog a reason to be attentive and focused during pace changes.

Step 1: After *Food Bowling* or *Out and Around a Cone*, turn away from your dog slowly and move away. As your dog comes up alongside you, take a couple of slow steps before presenting your hand for a *Jump to Hand* then *Jump to Food*, and *Food Bowling* for another round.

Step 2: Start as above, though instead of presenting your hand after a few steps, lean forward then take off running! After several steps, present your hand for *Jump to Hand*, then *Jump to Food* and start the game again with bowling or out and around.

"A slower pace shouldn't result in a flatter attitude or for the dog to disengage. Following up a slow pace with a burst of speed can build anticipation. The expectation of that burst builds a little bit of excitement that presents in a keenness or intensity even while in a slower pace, even while walking."

Step 3: You can add some unpredictability and challenge to this by instead of racing forward, turn away from your dog in a quick U-turn and run away several steps. When your dog catches up, *Jump to Hand, Jump to Food.*

Gradually extend the number of steps you take either in a slow pace or a fast past before *Jump to Hand/Jump to Food*, or turning and running for *Jump to Hand/Jump to Food* then bowl again. Or send to a cone instead of bowling to mix it up a bit!

Lunge Work for a More Consistent Gait

Despite our dog's enthusiasm and strong position, there may be some inconsistency in gait or an undesirable gait such as pacing.

Often, the on-going use of *Jump for Joy* (both hand and food), and cavaletti work, along with playing the games that encourage speed followed by collection, can eliminate any issues with pacing. And often by increasing or stabilizing the handler's pace, the dog can move into a trot. Sometimes though, a bit more intervention may be needed.

Lunging, long used in the equine world, can be modified to elicit and reinforce a more consistent gait and can often help a dog learn to trot rather than pace.

As in lunging a horse, the dog is moving in a large circle, independent of the handler to start. Unlike lunging a horse, the dog is "at liberty" or free of any line or tether.

Step 1: Teach your dog to move in a large circle around you.

There are many ways to teach a dog to move in a large circle around and away from you. I use cones to teach this as I will be using the cones as context for the rest of the exercise.

What is Pacing?

A pace, like a walk or trot, is a specific gait determined by the way a dog places their feet while moving forward through time and space. In a walk or trot, a dog's legs are moving opposite and diagonally from each other. When a dog is pacing, their feet and legs on either side of their body are moving in unison with each other. Their front right and rear right are moving in unison and their front left and rear left is moving in unison. This often creates a side to side rocking motion.

It is speculated that dogs that pace are conserving energy or are unable to provide a level of energy to perform a trot. There are likely many reasons a dog could start to pace. It could be due to excess weight, lack of conditioning, temporary low energy level, neurological issues, physical discomfort, growth spurts or this could just be a normal gait for your dog due to their structure. Before embarking on a training program to change your dog's pacing, check with a veterinarian to ensure there isn't a physical reason for the pacing.

1) Send your dog *Out and Around* a cone from a distance of 8-10 feet. Mark as they round the cone and bowl behind you to start again.

2) After a few reps, add a cone right next to the first and cue your dog to go *Out and Around*. Because the cones are close to each other, they will need to pass the second one to earn a marker. Always mark as they pass the last cone. Bowl your treat in the direction of travel you will want your dog to eventually move in - a large circle. Repeat for a couple of reps.

3) Continue to add cones, one right next to the other to encourage your dog to continue until the last cone. It's important to maintain your distance from the cones as we want to teach the dog to go out in a large circle around us. If your dog needs you close, then work on distance **from** the cone before continuing with distance **around all the cones**.

After marking, always bowl your treat in the direction your dog is traveling to encourage further movement in a circle.

Step 2: Once your dog is moving easily in a quarter circle around several cones next to each other, take every other cone, one or two cones at a time, and add them to the end of the circle. You are now expanding the circumference of the circle, not by adding new cones but by using the existing cones, to create wider spaces between the cones in the first quarter of the circle.

Continue to enlarge the circle using the existing cones until your dog can move around the outside of the circle.

Having your dog move in a large circle with the expectation of chasing a bowled treat will create some speed. The goal is that your dog trot around the cones, and not gallop or canter. If your dog is moving too fast, you can slow them by tossing the treat closer to them or even just over their shoulder for a few reps. When you see your dog start to trot fairly consistently, due to the expectation that the treat will be tossed closer to them, you can start to mark the trot before tossing your treat.

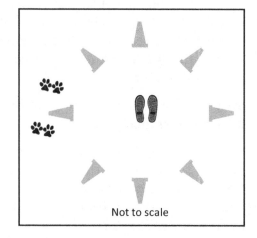

Not to scale

Step 3: Up to this point you have been in the center of the circle, marking and rewarding your dog for trotting. Outside of these sessions, you will have been working to increase or stabilize your speed. Now it's time to start to bring these two things together.

1) Send your dog out around the circle as in step 2 and mark and reward as your dog moves in a trot.

2) After this initial warm-up, as your dog trots around the circle, start to move toward the outside of the circle and the cones, just ahead of your dog. Be sure to maintain a consistent and appropriate speed. As your dog moves in alongside you, trotting for a few steps with you, mark with a *Jump to Hand*, reward with a *Jump to Food*, then food bowl another treat forward. Move back toward the middle of the circle, and repeat as your dog continues forward around the cones.

The previous steps will take a bit of time, don't rush this. Help your dog build the skill and pattern in trotting that they need. And allow yourself the time you need to build the speed and stamina that you require.

Step 4: Continue to eliminate your cones until you have longer stretches of area to heel. Generally, you won't go down to under 4 cones when practicing this exercise, though 2 cones and working in an oval is doable.

If your dog starts to forge or pace, you can send them around the next cone or you and your dog can do a 360 around the next cone before continuing or sending your dog out to go around in the circle again.

As is not uncommon in training, you will need to go back to the base exercise on occasion for maintenance. Be sure to work to maintain consistency and briskness in your speed as well. The goal is that 1) your dog learns to find the trot through muscle memory and experience with the exercise and 2) that you learn to maintain a speed that helps your dog to succeed at maintaining the trot.

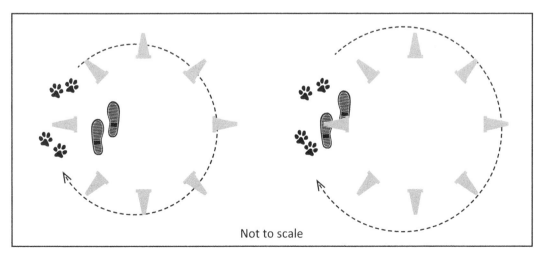

Not to scale

I Got Rhythm, I Got Music...

One reason a dog might pace is the handler's speed. The dog knows to stay with the handler, but the handler may be moving too slow for a trot and too fast for a walk. For some dog and handler teams, just changing speed may resolve the issue entirely. For others, it might not be the speed but the inconsistency of the handler's movement.

Even in using the lunging method, increasing or creating more consistency in the speed of the handler will likely be necessary. Knowing the handler's pace - how many "beats per minute" or BPMs they walk - is good information from which to learn to move at a speed that benefits both dog and handler. Once the handler knows the current BPM's they move at, they can work to increase it a little at time, using video to see how the change in speed affects their dog's gait.

There are metronome apps that can help keep time, and even websites that list the BPMs for songs, so that you can move to a particular song with the appropriate BPMs for you and your dog.

Notes:

CHAPTER 17:

Games Lead to Heeling, Heeling Leads to Games

Using the games to bring joy into your heelwork training is great! The end goal though is that your dog finds that same joy while heeling in the ring. Whether your sport is obedience, Rally, Rally-FrEe or musical freestyle. You can take little pieces of your sport and insert them into the games, just as you took little bits of heeling and inserted it into the games.

Obedience heeling pattern: We know there are always going to be certain skills included in a heeling pattern. You have your pace changes – normal, slow, and fast. You have your left, right and about turns, figure-8 and your halts. I recommend you leave your halts for last. These are easy to add. We want to focus on movement before we focus on stops.

Choose a part of the heeling pattern that includes no more than ten steps of heeling. Start with a game of *Food Bowling* and *Jump for Joy*. Add part of a heeling pattern, then *Jump to Hand* and back to *Food Bowling* to repeat with a different piece.

So a little bit of *Food Bowling*, into heeling a few steps, about turn, *Jump to Hand* and *Jump to Food*, *Food Bowling* or send *Out and Around a Cone* to start again! Gradually increase the number of steps of heeling before or after the element (turns, pace changes, etc.) you are practicing.

For a **Rally** or **Rally-FrEe** course: Start the game with a bit of *Food Bowling*. As you move forward in heel, perform a sign behavior followed by a few steps of heeling, then *Jump to Hand*, *Jump to Food*, bowl again. Gradually increase the number of signs your dog performs – ping-pong how many you work! Keep your dog wondering "Is it now? Is it now?" keeping them eager and ready for what comes next!

For your **Freestyle routines**, start your game of *Food Bowling* and *Jump for Joy*, perform a short sequence of 2-3 behaviors/transitions from your routine and back to *Jump to Hand, Jump to Food*, and *Food Bowling*.

For each of these, you can also work in your *Heel with Me! Play with Me!* game, your *Just Do It!* game or any of your dog's favorites – you can have a cone nearby to send *Out and Around a Cone* to start the games. The key is that we bookend the work with the familiar games. Games lead to heeling and heeling leads to games.

Setting Up in Heel and Adding the Halt

I highly recommend having a separate cue for your dog to move into a set-up in heel in a sit. The work that you have been doing up to this point has been to build a moving heel. We want your dog to find value in moving with you in heel. We have been using a cue that means: Move with me in heel, using your rear to lift your chest and to remain next to me in an accurate position.

These are all different criteria than what we want from a dog that is sitting in heel. This is why for most of the games and exercises we have not asked the dog to start in a set-up position of sitting next to us.

You can use a sit platform to teach your dog your set-up in heel cue, the same way we used the standing platform. The size of the platform tells the dog what they should do. If the platform is large enough to stand then they should stand, if the platform is only large enough to sit then they should sit.

For a dog that understands what to do with a platform, teaching a cue for the dog to set-up in heel is as easy as putting a sit platform next to you, tossing a cookie, and giving your new set-up cue. Once you add the cue, you would start the process of removing the platform.

Back Chaining with Games

This section is fairly technical so you might grab a cup of tea or coffee (or glass of wine!) and give yourself some time to go through it. More than once would be good. I know that for many of the exercises you might get away with glancing at the text and then trying it yourself. You won't be able to do that with this exercise.

When integrating your joyful heeling into the other work you'll be doing in the ring, back chaining can be a powerful tool to teach your dog about delayed reinforcement and using the games as part of the reinforcement. Being able to take your hand touch into the ring as a familiar part of games and the end of a sequence of behaviors is invaluable.

Back chaining is a process in which you reinforce the last behavior in a chain and then add each previous behavior sequentially, always and only rewarding after the last and final behavior in the sequence/chain. You want to use only fluent behaviors when applying back chaining.

In a chain or sequence of behaviors of A B C D, the last behavior in the sequence is D. That is where you will start your back chain.

The Process:

Start by rewarding after "D" a couple of times so your dog starts to expect that reward comes after "D." That *reward* is going to be your games multiplied - The longer the chain the greater the reinforcement in duration, quality, and quantity. What behaviors A, B, C, and D represent depends on your sport.

If your sport is obedience, then the ABCD sequence might be:

A: Set-up in heel

B: Heel forward 6 steps

C: Right turn

D: Heel forward 4 steps

Your back chain would be:

D (heel forward 4 steps), then into games

Then C (right turn) D (Heel forward) and then into games.

Then B (heel forward 6 steps) C (right turn) D (Heel forward) and then into games.

Then A (set-up in heel) B (heel forward) C (right turn) D (Heel forward) and then into games.

Obedience: Think of your obedience exercises that include heelwork and create your chains out of those. You can change the order frequently to start so the dog doesn't become stuck on any one pattern. Once you are ready to work the actual chains that you'll be performing in the ring (your obedience patterns, your Rally-FrEe courses and your freestyle routines), you will want to stay with those same order of behaviors. Work to have your heeling be the final behavior in the chain just before your games. That way your heeling will become part of reinforcement for the sequence that preceded it.

Rally and Rally-FrEe: If your sport is Rally-FrEe or AKC Rally® Virtual Program then A B C D would be a sequence of signs from your upcoming course. If you are competing in live Rally trials and don't know the course ahead of time, you'll be working using random signs but changing them frequently so your dog learns to work for longer stretches without reinforcement and that sequences of signs always end in fun and games.

While your course may be 12-20 signs, I don't recommend that you do more than 5-6 signs at a time. Six signs is actually 12 behaviors when you include the heeling between the signs.

This is not only an excellent way to prepare for competition but also a good way to practice back chaining if you are new to it, as the signs and the order of the signs give you a visual map.

For Freestyle, you would work short sequences leading to the last behavior in the sequence then games.

Below is an example of back chaining a freestyle sequence. The sequence is heel forward, spin, sidepass, paw lift.

A: Heel forward

B: Spin

C: Sidepass

D: Paw lift

Your back chain would be:

D (paw lift in heel), then into games

Then C (sidepass) D (paw lift in heel) and then into games.

Then B (spin) C (sidepass) D (paw lift in heel) and then into games.

Then the full sequence of A (heel forward) B (spin) C (sidepass) D (paw lift in heel) and then into games.

Once you start practicing your set sequences – such as your obedience exercises, or freestyle routines, you want to only include behaviors in your back chains that are fluent, or at least fluent in the environment that you are building your back chain.

Keep your chains short, no more than 4-6 behaviors and sometimes fewer. You aren't going to back chain your whole routine or all of your obedience exercises or your whole Rally-FrEe course, just your sequences. I try to always back chain my ring entrance, my first and last sequences from my routine and at least 2 - 3 other sequences. I will also overlap my back chains to build new "start points" for chains. (ABCD) and (EFGH) becomes (CDEF).

Because the start of the chain allows the dog to be able to predict when a reward will happen, overlapping your chains continues to create new start points for your dog to predict reward. Each new start point reinforces the previous chain or sequence.

This allows the dog to willingly work for longer periods of time without reinforcement as the practiced back chains tell him that reinforcement is coming....at the end of the chain.

Whether you are experienced at back chaining or are new to the concept, as with everything else in training, it is wise to practice first without your dog. Know your sequence like the back of your hand before trying to put it into a back chain.

Back chains can be a bit confusing, so it helps to use a "cheat sheet." The first one is a sample, and the second is for you to fill out and use for your obedience patterns, freestyle sequences, or Rally courses. Note that in this back chain of part of an obedience pattern, the "set up in heel" only occurs once as part of the full and final sequence. That means your dog will be standing when he starts to heel for each of the parts of the back chain. You can accomplish that by asking your dog for a stand stay and then moving into a position that places him in heel position before moving forward.

Forward Chain — Sample	
Behavior A	Set up in Heel
Behavior B	Heel forward normal pace 6 steps
Behavior C	Right turn
Behavior D	Heel forward normal pace 4 steps
Behavior E	Heel forward slow pace 4 steps

Back chain worksheet					
E. Heel forward slow pace 4 steps	Reward Event/Games				
D. Heel forward normal pace 4 steps	E. Heel forward slow pace 4 steps	Reward Event/Games			
C. Right turn	D. Heel forward normal pace 4 steps	E. Heel forward slow pace 4 steps	Reward Event/Games		
B. Heel forward normal pace 6 steps	C. Right turn	D. Heel forward normal pace 4 steps	E. Heel forward slow pace 4 steps	Reward Event/Games	
A. Set up in Heel	B. Heel forward normal pace 6 steps	C. Right turn	D. Heel forward normal pace 4 steps	E. Heel forward slow pace 4 steps	Reward Event/ Games

Forward Chain	
Behavior A	
Behavior B	
Behavior C	
Behavior D	
Behavior E	

Back chain worksheet					
E.	Reward Event/Games				
D.	E.	Reward Event/Games			
C.	D.	E.	Reward Event/Games		
B.	C.	D.	E.	Reward Event/Games	
A.	B.	C.	D.	E.	Reward Event/ Games

Notes:

CHAPTER 18:
Maintaining Criteria and Putting it All Together

The games and exercises in this book help you to create the criteria you want, both technical and emotional. Training is all about criteria. If you don't know what your criteria are, you won't know when to mark and reward when your dog meets your criteria. You won't know how to build it and you won't know how to maintain it. You have three tasks in training behaviors:

Identify and create your criteria

Build value in the criteria

Be critical of the criteria

For the technical criteria, you might ask: is it straight, is it close, is it tight, is the shoulder or head where I want it? What duration do I want? Is my dog looking up at me? Each of these is trained independently from each other before bringing them together into the end resulting behavior. While some will certainly overlap in training sessions, it's important to identify the exact criterion you are reinforcing. "Lumping" or trying to reinforce too many components all at once can result in unfocused sessions and ill-defined criteria for the dog.

Emotional criteria might include relaxed yet animated body posture, alert and attentive, an appropriate level of energy, showing a desire to engage, and what I'll call "bright eyes."

Once you've identified your criteria, you want to create it. For the technical criteria, this is where aids come in - platforms, gates, or reinforcement strategies. It's up to the handler to create and communicate to the dog what the technical criteria are.

Many of the games address emotional criteria - that the dog finds pleasure and joy in heelwork - even with the more technical exercises and games where our intent is to build our position criteria.

Now that you've identified and created your criteria, you need to then build value in those criteria. Without value in the criteria, the dog will never learn to choose it, to create it on their own, to make it happen, and to continue to perform it. Building value in all of the criteria that we desire as part of that behavior is what allows the dog to bring the components together into the end behavior of joyful heeling.

Building value includes using a variety of reinforcers – high-value food, *Fast Food* versus *Fine Dining*, toys, play, tug, and of course all of the games outlined in this book that your dog has learned to love. A longer reward event – 30-90 sec of reinforcement with praise – is more valuable than a cursory treat, or quick tug. Your duration of reward, the time you spend with the games, should be as long as the time spent working.

The higher the value of the reinforcer, the happier the dog is to perform the behavior and all of its criteria. All of the games we've been playing have one goal – to bring joy to your dog and build value in the behavior we attach it to – heeling.

This is where **being critical** of criteria starts to come into play. When it comes to the emotional side, I think we are pretty good at determining whether our dogs are in a happy emotional state. And if not, we know how to create that and then associate it with both the behavior and the cue.

In regard to the technical exercises, if it's not what you want, then don't mark and reward it! Sounds easy right!? Not so much!

Training can be messy! Especially when we start to remove the props that have created those technical criteria for us! Often, we need to shift criteria on the fly. When the dog has met the criteria with confidence 3-4 times in a row, time to ask for more, right? Right!

"You get what you reward and not what you cue."

Too often though we don't know what that looks like. We need to **define our criteria**. What is "more"? More of what? So we end up marking whatever they give us next even if it wasn't as "good" as the previous. Having a very clear picture in your mind and being able to articulate that picture clearly to the dog is imperative if we want to improve the dog's performance of specific criteria. This is true for all training, but is especially important for behaviors that include precision and accuracy, or removing aids and maintaining behavior.

For our heeling positions, if the criterion is "close" there are several ways we can communicate that to the dog. We can use props such as platforms or training gates. We can use the timing of our marker. We can use the placement of our rewards. But even in the use of these aids, if we haven't defined "close" or "straight" or other elements clearly in our own mind, we will be unable to make it clear to the dog. We can end up rewarding something that doesn't meet our criteria. In our lack of clarity, the criteria in the dog's mind have shifted.

I'm not referring to consciously changing criteria or deciding to lower criteria because it hasn't been met a couple of times in a row – I'm referring to how we often mark and reward criteria that we don't want. Or how we drop or lower a criterion when we should be raising it.

It's easy to allow our criteria to get wishy-washy in the midst of a training session especially if we haven't clearly articulated what those criteria are. "Close" is not enough of a definition. "Close equals a hand's width from my pant seam" is a more articulate criterion or definition. This gives a clear picture of what is the criterion for reward and what is not.

Criteria shifts are one of the most difficult concepts for trainers to apply. That piece of training where we need to push the limits to get to the next level, the next little bits of criteria that take us closer to the end behavior, the final product. Or where we need to increase confidence and understanding by lowering our criteria for another couple of reps. But how do we know if we are asking for too much and need to lower our criteria or not enough and need to raise our criteria?

When and how to increase criteria is a process that many trainers struggle with. It's often described as a linear or stair-step process, yet when you are in the throes of it, it feels anything but linear, even, for the best of trainers. There is often a little bit of guessing that goes on before sliding into a place where you feel you made the right choice.

That doesn't mean you don't want to strive for a clean, linear process.

While we understand how to tell the dog they did something right (mark and reward) we often don't recognize when to tell the dog they provided an incorrect response, and to try again.

Once my dog is showing some skill and understanding of my criterion, I want to be critical of what earns reward (the dog is a hand's width from the seam of my pants, for example). I want to select for that criterion and only that criterion. If that criterion is met, the dog is reinforced. If that criterion is not met, despite both a strong reward history and a history of correctness, I wait… or negate. I

"Clear communication is reinforcing."

let the dog figure out why there is no marker or reinforcement (or next cue), and let them correct it, or release them to start again, indicating to the dog no reward for that effort, time to try again.

In determining whether to **lower criteria**, if the dog responds with two errors in a row, I've made it too hard, asked for too much – so I lower criteria. – two errors in a row can indicate a lack of understanding. Or if too much time has passed with no effort or response, I've made the criterion too hard. For me, that's no more than a count of 5. Our goal is to provide appropriate information so that neither of these occurs often. Sometimes though we need to adjust our criteria to provide more clear information to our dogs.

Lowering criteria, or making it easier for the dog to succeed following errors might include putting the platform back down, or using a different prop, or marking earlier before possibly making another error.

Once I see confidence and predictability in a specific criterion, that tells me my dog understands that piece of the behavior and I can **increase criteria**. If I stay there too long, both my dog and I will get stuck. Raising criteria might be removing the platform or withholding the marker for a little better position or longer duration.

Part of why increasing criteria can be so difficult is that we, the handlers, are heavily reinforced by our dog's correctness, that celebration and sense of success we feel when our dog responds with confidence and predictability. That reinforcement strengthens our behavior to continue to ask for the same criteria...again, and again. And because our dog has no idea that what he's doing is simply a means to an end, continually reinforced criteria become stronger and stronger until it becomes very difficult to push through it, to improve the behavior, to get to the final product.

One of my favorite analogies is Kathy Sdao's, equating criteria shifts to the groove in a record (yep, we are dating ourselves). For those of you that remember LPs or vinyl records, if the needle gets stuck in a groove, it will play the same thing over and over – it "skips". And unless we put a little pressure on the needle, it's unable to advance. Unlike the success of our dogs, a skipping record becomes irritating and so we quickly apply that pressure to be able to listen to the rest of the song. Not enough to scratch the record, just enough to slip into the next groove.

Progress doesn't happen without going outside of our comfort zone just a little, just enough to progress to the next set of successes that will take us closer to our goals.

This is what we want to become better at: Once the criteria are defined and predictable, "less than" doesn't earn the reward. If necessary, we can shift criteria downward, but with true cause – if the incorrect responses (meaning they don't meet criteria) are more than two in a row or uncertainty results in latency, then split the difference to the next lower criterion. Again, if the dog has shown understanding through consistent and predictably strong responses, maintain your criteria unless there is true cause. This might include the appearance of frustration, confusion, or disengagement. If these things occur your previous criteria may not be as strong as your think – so time to rethink.

In all parts of the process, identifying criteria, creating criteria, building value in criteria, and maintaining the criteria, we need to be both clear and critical of our criteria and what we reward. The more clearly you articulate the criteria to yourself and to your dog, the greater value you can build into those criteria. The more critical you are in those criteria the more quickly the dog will be able to take on the responsibility of providing it. Clear communication is reinforcing. This will become more and more important as the dog starts to merge the joy or "emotional criteria" with the "technical criteria." You want to maintain both so that our dogs can willingly and joyfully, with precision and accuracy, engage in the behavior of heeling when given the opportunity.

GLOSSARY

Antecedent: something that occurs prior to behavior

CER: acronym for Conditioned Emotional Response, an emotional response that is elicited due to a learned association with a stimulus

Cue: something that prompts behavior, a predictor of reinforcement

Criteria: the standards or requirements of a behavior or action being reinforced

Criterion: singular of criteria

Duration: the length of time before behavior terminates

Fast Food: a way to provide reinforcement, several treats in a row in rapid succession

Fine Dining: a way to provide reinforcement, several treats in a row in slow succession

HER: acronym for Happy Emotional Response

Inside turn: a change of direction for the dog-and-handler team where the dog is on the "inside" of the turn (dog on left, left turn or dog on right, right turn)

Latency: the period of time, or delay after a cue and before the behavior occurs

Luring: a method of training, using something the dog will follow to elicit behavior

Outside turn: a change of direction for the dog-and-handler team where the dog is on the "outside" of the turn (dog on left, right turn or dog on right, left turn)

Ping Ponging: a term describing a back and forth pattern between two sets of criteria

Pivot: a 90-degree turn where the dog's front feet are the pivot point

Proofing: a process of adding layers of difficulty to generalize learned behaviors under a variety of circumstances

Props: used to describe training aids that help communicate criteria

Reps: short for repetitions

Reinforcement: causes an increase in the quality or frequency of a behavior

Shaping: a method of training where the dog is reinforced for small increments of behavior toward an end goal behavior

Training gates: the name of a low barrier made of wire panels and used as a training aid. Developed by the author to create a guide in communicating specific criteria.

RESOURCES AND ACKNOWLEDGMENTS

Many have contributed to my own education and been invaluable resources for me both in writing this book and how I practice the art and science of training, more specifically how I teach heeling. Some I know personally and am grateful to have in my life. Others I have never met yet still have greatly impacted how I train. Many are referenced in this book and listed below, though not all.

A very special and heartfelt thank you goes to graphic artist, Teresa Hall whose art graces the cover and the beginning of each section of this book. She is responsible for the wonderful layout, diagrams and graphics and kept me moving forward in this project. Thank you for your encouragement and patience as we navigated this "first ever" for both of us!

And to Gail Beerman, editor-in-chief! Your time and talent are much appreciated! All in the midst of a busy litter of puppies!

Special thanks to Esther Zimmerman and her penchant for clarity.

To Denise Fenzi, for seeing something in me as a trainer that I didn't see in myself and giving me the opportunity, confidence, and resolve to think that I had anything worth saying in a book. I am thankful to have you in my corner.

And I would be remiss not to acknowledge the impact Diane Balkavich has had on my choices in training methods. My friend, my mentor, my inspiration. You are missed.

And to Kashi, I promise to do better.

Thank you to the following resources whose wealth of knowledge, expertise and experience is enough to make your head spin!

Amy Cook, Ph.D.
> The Play Way
> Online courses, seminars and workshops
> **Playwaydogs.com**

Cassandra Hartman
> Cassandra's Canines - Mind and Body Connection
> Online courses, seminars and workshops, instructional videos
> **Cassandrascanines.ca**

Dawn Jecs
> Choose to Heel© Dog Training System
> Author: *"Choose to Heel"*

Deborah Jones, Ph.D.

Online courses, seminars, workshops, instructional DVDs

Author: "*Clicker Fun: Dog Tricks and Games Using Positive Reinforcement*"

"*The Focused Puppy*" co-authored with Judy Keller

"*In Focus*" co-authored with Judy Keller

"*Click Here for a Well-Trained Dog*"

"*Dog Sports Skills Series*" Books 1-4 co-authored with Denise Fenzi

Book 1: Developing Engagement and Relationship,

Book 2: Motivation

Book 3: Play

Book 4: Focus and Engage

"*Cooperative Care: Seven Steps to Stress-Free Husbandry*"

K9infocus.com

Denise Fenzi

Fenzi Dog Sports Academy

Online courses, webinars and self-study options

Author: "*Dog Sports Skills Series*" Books 1-4 co-authored with Deborah Jones, Ph.D.,

Book 1: Developing Engagement and Relationship,

Book 2: Motivation

Book 3: Play,

Book 4: Focus and Engage

"*Beyond the Backyard*"

"*Beyond the Basics*"

"*Train the Dog in Front of You*"

"*Blogger Dog, Britto*"

"*Conversations with Raika*"

Thedogathlete.com

Thehighdrivedog.com

Denisefenzi.com

Hannah Branigan

Wonder Pups Training

Drinking from the Toilet Podcast

Online courses, seminars, workshops, instructional DVDs

Author: "*Awesome Obedience*"

Hannahbranigan.dog

Kathy Sdao, M.A.
    Applied Animal Behaviorist
    Bright Spot Training
    Webinars, seminars, consultations, educational DVDs
    Author: *"Plenty in Life is Free"*
    Kathysdao.com

Ken Ramirez
    Chief Training Officer of Karen Pryor Clicker Training (KPCT)
    Seminars, courses, consultations
    Lead Educator at "The Ranch: Karen Pryor National Training Center"
    Author: *"Animal Training: Successful Animal Management through Positive Reinforcement"*
    "The Eye of the Trainer: Animal Training, Transformation, and Trust"
    Kenramireztraining.com

Laura Romanik
    Radiant Competitive Obedience
    Seminars, classes, consultations
    Author: *"Heeling Log"*
    "Go Bop!"
    Lauraromanik.com

Lori Stevens
    Seattle TTouch
    Online courses, seminars and workshops, instructional DVDs
    Seattlettouch.com

Michele Pouliot
    Online courses, seminars and workshops, instructional DVDs
    Director of Training and Research at Guide Dogs for the Blind, Retired
    Michelepouliot.com

Morten Edgvart and Cecilie Koste
    Canis Clicker Training
    Authors of *"Clicker Training: The 4 Secret of Becoming a Supertrainer"*
    Canisclickertraining.com

Recommended Conferences, Online Schools and Training Camps:

Clicker Expo - Karen Pryor Clicker Training
Fenzi Dog Sports Academy
Fenzi Dog Sports Academy Training Camps
The Ranch: Karen Pryor National Training Center
The Art and Science of Animal Training Conference

PHOTO CREDITS

Page 3 upper right................................Dick Capello

Page 4 lower left ....Dean Lake

Page 5 upper right................................Jessie Meyer

Page 6 lower left ....Dick Capello

Page 7 upper left.................................Libbye Miller

Page 11 upper left ....Darienne Kraeker

Page 12 upper left ....Mike McGann

Page 16 lower right ....Sharon Gretch

Page 17 upper right ....MaRyka Smith

Page 23 lower right ....Lonnie Berger

Page 26 compilation upper left..............Carolina Bibiloni

Page 26 compilation lower left ....Chris Anderson

Page 26 compilation upper center..........Mike McGann

Page 26 compilation lower center..........Monica Anthony

Page 26 compilation upper right............Mary Stafford

Page 26 compilation lower right............Mary Stafford

Page 27 lower right sequence ....Sharon Gretch

Page 28 upper sequence ....Julie Fanery

Page 28 center right sequence ....Teresa Hall

Page 29 upper right..............................Dick Capello

Page 29 center right ....Dick Capello

Page 29 lower right ....Julie Flanery

Page 33 lower right ....Adam Skandarani

Page 37 lower right ....Kelly Ladouceur

Page 40 upper right..............................Teresa Hall

Page 41 center sequence........................Teresa Hall

Page 45 lower left................................Chance Felisky, Swiftrun Photography

Page 48 upper left ....Teresa Hall

Made in United States
Orlando, FL
10 August 2023

35946815R00104